Published in 2003 by Caxton Editions
20 Bloomsbury Street
London WC1B 3JH
a member of the Caxton Publishing Group

Designed and produced for Caxton Editions
by Open Door Limited
Rutland, United Kingdom

Editing: Mary Morton
DIGITAL IMAGERY © copyright 2003 PhotoDisc Inc.

Title: The Art of Oriental Face Reading
ISBN: 1 84067 446 6

THE ART OF ORIENTAL

FACE READING

SUE WOODD

CAXTON EDITIONS

CONTENTS

CONTENTS

INTRODUCTION

Knowing others is intelligence
Knowing yourself is true wisdom
Mastering others is strength
Mastering yourself is true power.

Tao Te Ching – Lao Tzu

A FORGOTTEN ART REVIVED

When people first hear about using the art of visual or touch diagnosis to determine a person's health, constitution and basic nature, they often discount the idea for a number of reasons based on habit or convention. They may consider it to be non-scientific, too much like fortune telling or even too psychic for their taste. They do not realise they are using diagnosis themselves all the time, for it plays a significant part in how we communicate and inter-relate.

Diagnosis gives us an insight into, and an understanding of, human nature and creates a deeper, more satisfying communication between individuals. We are consciously and subconsciously making evaluations all the time about the health, character and attitudes of those around us, based solely on what we see and sense through our gut feeling or intuition.

We may inquire about someone's health by saying "You look tired" or "Aren't you feeling well?" We may judge someone's emotional condition by thinking they seem happy or they seem depressed. We may assess their mental attitude by saying "you don't believe me, do you?". Simply becoming aware of and identifying these impressions are all forms of diagnosis.

In the East, these evaluations have developed into a highly refined system of character and health diagnosis. Western forms of diagnosis deal mainly with symptoms and conditions using modern scientific technology. In comparison the oriental system seeks out and exposes causal factors, which are a collation of the person's total past involvements in all aspects of their life. It makes visible future directions and potential for creating health and happiness, and restoring balance. It enables us to see problems that are beginning to develop and affords us the opportunity to use preventative measures to re-direct their course. Healing methods used during the stage where difficulty is developing are simpler, easier and more harmonious with the body and life process than those measures which become necessary once the problem has fully manifested itself, giving the person time to change those aspects of his or her life that are creating disharmony, increased stress or contributing to the development of the sickness.

The medicine of the Far East is among the oldest in the world and it can teach us a great deal that can be practically applied today, based on the experience of thousands of years. Furthermore, it is complementary to the kind of medicine currently practised in the West. Here are some examples:

EASTERN	WESTERN
Takes into account the whole picture	Focuses in on a particular aspect
Looks to find the cause producing the symptom	Treats/removes the symptoms
Looks at nature to see how we have deviated from its laws	Uses scientific methods and technology to diagnose
Seeks to restore balance or ease	Looks for illness or "dis-ease"
Preventative/economical	Symptomatic/expensive
Observes changes in energy even before specific symptoms occur	Observes symptoms or a change in structure
Takes into account our uniqueness, constitution and ancestral history	Uses national averages and statistics
Uses diet, breathing and other lifestyle changes so the individual can take responsibility and participate in their own health.	Seeks to provide the individual with medical care
Emphasis is placed on healing	Emphasis is placed on cure

The standard oriental writings on the causes of disease link health and well-being to diet, activities, attitude and environment. No single aspect is isolated; biological, psychological and spiritual factors all contribute to the whole.

The practitioner, adviser or teacher gives practical advice about changes of lifestyle that can help to rectify problems at source. By understanding our basic character, nature, strengths and weaknesses, the best and most unique course of action can be taken.

These include such things as:

- *our constitution, including the strength and weaknesses of parents*
- *our environment*
- *foods and liquids consumed*
- *activity, sports and general lifestyle*
- *our present condition as manifested in behaviour, voice, perception, face posture, skin colour, condition of blood, organs and nervous system.*

Below: biological, psychological and spiritual factors all contribute to our well-being.

HEALING is the result of putting right the wrongs in our relationship with others and with our bodies, minds, emotions and instincts, and re-organising and re-integrating those aspects that may have become separated or have been in conflict. This implies self-empowerment and alignment which enables us to express fully our unique potential as human beings in all aspects of our lives. Often this can be an uncomfortable process but it is always an empowering one.

As we face up to aspects of ourselves that we were unaware of or were unable to acknowledge, we begin a process of discovery and our entire being is given permission to change on whatever level is necessary. As we release old patterns, blocked emotions and rigid ways of being we gain a new sense of respect for all our aspects and rhythms. This exciting process involves waking up, learning and surrendering to our inner and outer experiences.

CURING implies someone or something external working with the intention of eliminating disease, symptoms or crisis through drugs, surgery, and psychotherapy in an attempt to control our inner and outer experiences rather than us learning from them.

An example of how the effect of imbalance/stress in the body can be reflected in the face:
The nose corresponds to the nervous system and the spine. The muscles in the back, shoulders and neck and face are intimately connected. If there is stress on one side of the body, often coming from somewhere along the spine, our posture and all the muscles of the face will reflect that stress. If the stress is severe and remains for some time, it will even pull the nose off centre in the direction of the stress.

An example of internal change being manifested in the face:
The condition of the heart can be seen in the tip of the nose. Alcohol is a very yin substance in oriental nutrition; it causes the blood vessels to dilate and go red. If this process of dilatation is going on within the body the nose will redden showing how an internal change can be reflected in the face.

It is important to use this book wisely. It is not intended to replace professional health care, so do not try to take over a doctor's role. Help yourself where you can but seek medical advice where you cannot.

When an enlightened person hears of the Tao,
they immediately begin to embody it.
When an average person hears of the Tao, they half believe it and half doubt it.
When a foolish person hears of the Tao, they laugh out loud.
If they didn't it would not be the Tao.

Tao Te Ching – Lao Tzu

THE TAO (PRONOUNCED DOW)

In the orient they have always expressed their ideas through the language of nature and the study of its laws so it is easy for even the poorest and uneducated to grasp its concepts.

Taoism dates back over 5,000 years, and simply means "the harmonious way", which is not a religion but a way of life that aims to live and work in perfect harmony with nature's laws and to achieve a state of balance between mind, body and spirit.

The philosophy of the Tao can be explained by four main concepts:

* *the dynamic principles of yin and yang*

* *chi – our vital energy and life force*

* *the meridian and organ system*

* *the five transformations of energy.*

Right: the meridian points in the face and head.

It can be used as an effective personal tool for unlocking the mysteries of life and harnessing universal powers to regulate and enhance our energy and serve the needs of humanity, experiencing its power in practice rather than it just being an academic theory.

THE DYNAMIC PRINCIPLE OF YIN AND YANG

Everyday we acquire new knowledge, but this knowledge will not remain in us unless we live in harmony with nature's laws. Living in harmony with these laws is to possess the true science of life, so true wisdom will bestow itself within us.

Omraam Aivanhov

In order to fully grasp the philosophy of oriental medicine and diagnosis it is essential to understand fully the concept of yin and yang, and how it affects the human body.

Imagine a dynamic energy or life force. It cannot know its magnificence or what it is if there is nothing to compare itself with, hence the one energy becomes two. Without having an awareness of large, how do we know what small is? Without summer, how can we appreciate the concept of winter? These complementary opposites help us to feel and develop our own relative experiences.

This polarity is the basic premise of all existence. Yin and yang are expressed in the classic black and white symbol, which represents two opposite yet complementary energies or forces working together to create balance. The yang principle is active while the yin is passive, yet nothing is purely yin or purely yang. Although fully independent energies they cannot exist without each other. The classic yin and yang symbol shows the small black (yin) dot within the white area (yang) and the white dot (yang) within the black area (yin).

Above: the yin and yang symbol, a familiar image.

Right: in the East these polarities are seen as a cycle of spiralling energy.

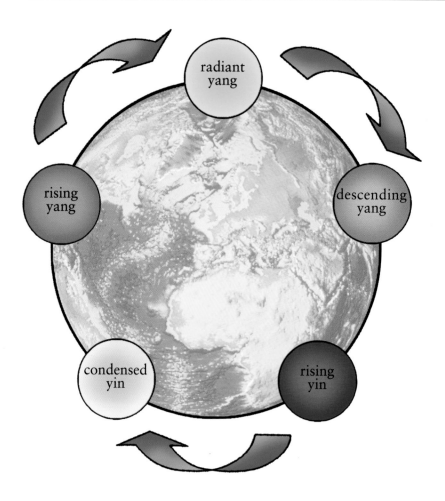

These energies are constantly moving, changing and transforming and understanding the ebb and flow of these natural forces is the key to balance and harmony. Imbalance occurs when there is resistance to this natural ebb and flow which causes an excess or deficiency of either yin or yang. Just as the seasons of the year are constantly moving from summer (active) yang to winter (passive) yin, so we too need this cycle of rejuvenation.

This is also true for our physical, emotional and mental states, for the food we eat, for the environment in which we live and for our lifestyles and activities. Oriental diagnosis is based on these elements.

In the West, these are explained as being the linear polarities of life whereas in Eastern philosophy these polarities are seen as a cycle of spiralling energy. Yang is likened to the sun and the forces of heaven and yin is likened to the moon and earth's energy.

Traditional Chinese medicine uses
the following complementary
principles in diagnosis:

YANG	YIN
Heaven	Earth
Sun	Moon
Male	Female
Hot	Cold
Dry	Damp
Active	Passive
Movement	Rest
Hard	Soft
Rising	Sinking
Light	Dark

Below: Oriental diagnosis is based on yin and yang principles.

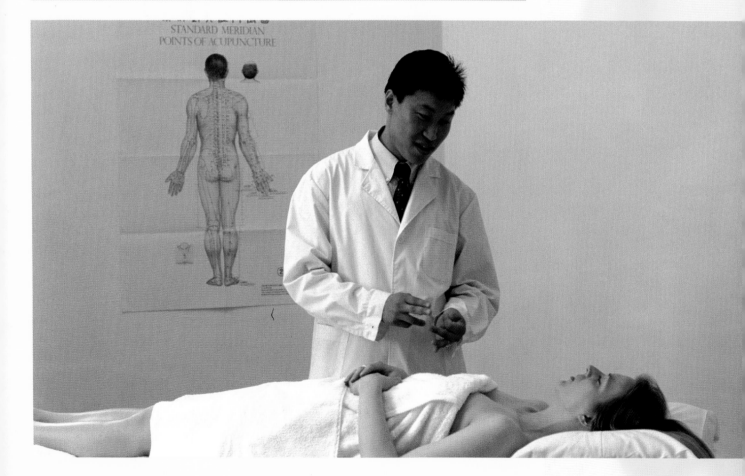

CONSTITUTIONAL QUALITIES OF YIN AND YANG IN ORIENTAL DIAGNOSIS

Oriental diagnosis goes on to explain the effect of these energies on our body. For example, the movement of yang makes food grow down into the soil and our body, muscles and features contract. When the yin earth force is predominant, it causes the food to grow up out of it, our organs to expand and our features to move apart. We come from heaven to earth so we are yang when small, active and compact. As we remain on earth we expand, slow down and grow older and more yin.

Listed below are some of the Yin and Yang constitutional qualities used in Oriental diagnosis:

PHYSICAL TYPE	YANG QUALITY	YIN QUALITY
Areas	Head	Body
Eyes	Small, round, close-set	Larger, almond wide-set
Nose	Broad, thick	Narrow, thin
Mouth	Small, tight	Broad, loose
Chin	Square	Pointed
Ears	Thick, large	Pointed
Bones	Wide, heavy	Narrow, light
Psychology	Practical, time-orientated	Theoretical, spatial
Life expression	Building, management, sports, business	Arts, science, writing, research, computers

VITAL ENERGY – CHI

From ancient times, Eastern medicine and diagnosis have considered the universe to be comprised of energy in various stages of vibration and manifestation. The air we breathe, the food we eat and the houses we build are all energy but in different forms. This energy is known by many different names. In China it is called "chi" or "qi", in Japan "ki" and in India "prana". In the West, the nearest translation is "vital energy" or "life-force", which in the human sense can mean our power and vitality.

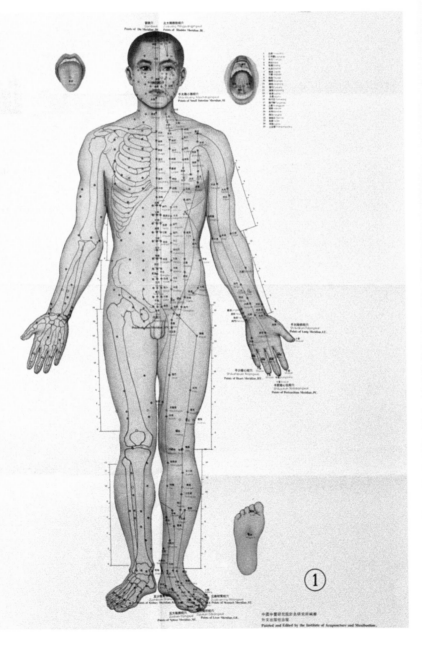

Left: our internal chi flows throughout the face and body in channels called meridians.

If this life force within us flows freely between mind, emotions and body, our lives flow easily. We can adapt to change, process difficulties and heal from illness.

WHAT CAN WE DO TO NOURISH AND CULTIVATE OUR CHI

Chi is strongly influenced by our mental and emotional attitude. We should cultivate strong positive beliefs and a clear emotional life. We need plenty of fresh air, gentle exercise and good quality food so we can open ourselves to the nourishment of the natural world. It is so important with all the advance in technology to maintain this balance.

Chi kung (qi gong) are energy cultivation exercises, and t'ai chi and yoga are excellent to build up our life-force.

Meridians

Our internal chi flows throughout the face and body in channels called meridians. These nourish specific organs and systems in the body and flow out to nourish every cell. They often travel significant distances from the organs they nourish.

For example, the large intestine meridian (one each side of the body) begins at the tip of the index finger and ends at the side of the nose in the grooves at each side of the nostril. When the large intestine cannot adequately eliminate, energy moves upwards, along the meridian to the nose and sinuses resulting in mucus congestion, headaches and other discomforts in the head.

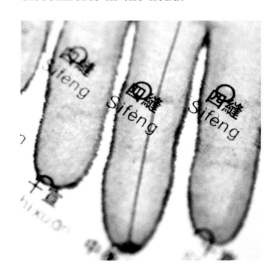

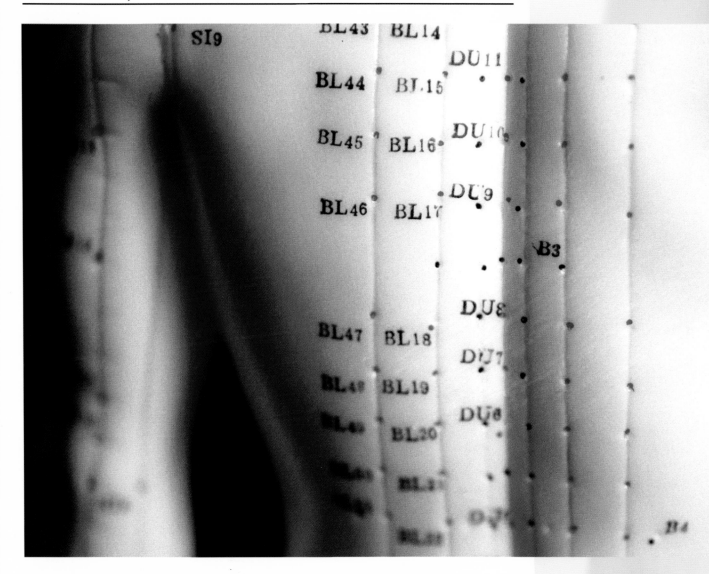

Pressure points

These are points along the meridians where the chi can be influenced by pressure (or needle insertion as in acupuncture). They act as gateways into a person's energy and can be used to affect the internal environment, influencing chi strength and circulation, acting as "circuit breakers" if the meridian is blocked or out of balance.

Doa yin (Chinese) or Do-in (Japanese) are simple massage techniques performed on the head and face to stimulate these pressure points calming overactive chi, uplifting weak chi and dispersing blocked chi. (see p.89)

Above: pressure points are points along the meridians where the chi can be influenced by pressure (or needle insertion as in acupuncture).

Right: the five elements are descriptions of chi in different stages of change.

The book of living Nature is not just an inventory of insects, minerals and plants written by man but a deep knowing of life as it bursts forth, flows and correlates between the different planes within ourselves and the universe around us.

Omraam Aivanhov

Understanding the philosophy of the five transformations of energy (often referred to as the five elements) is the cornerstone of oriental medicine and diagnosis.

The cyclic interplay between yin and yang is expressed and manifested in nature, our environment and our bodies. This change manifests through five phases or movements of energy that can be experienced during the seasons and throughout our daily cycles. These five elements are descriptions of chi (energy) in different stages of change, each element having its own characteristics, properties and qualities. This process can be easily understood on both an intuitive and a common-sense level. A common expression for it in English is "being in our element".

WOOD energy is the rising and expanding energy, manifested in spring and in the morning.

FIRE energy is the peak of outward or dispersing energy, manifested in full summer and during the middle of the day.

EARTH energy is centred and balanced when it starts to turn downwards and back to the centre of the earth, manifested in late summer and during the afternoon.

METAL is the consolidating and gathering energy as we prepare for autumn and return home in the evening.

WATER is the quiet, resting time enabling change and rejuvenation to take place, in winter and during the night.

In traditional medicine and diagnosis these elements and forms of energy are aligned on:

- *the physical level – to the different organs, the systems they govern, our senses and even the quality of the voice. (Refer to the section on the voice)*

- *the emotional level – to the emotions we feel (Refer to the section on the face and the emotions)*

- *the mental level – to our life challenges and ways of thinking. (Refer to the section on the shapes of the forehead).*

Our goal in diagnosis is to see how these elements manifest in our nature and on our face and use them to align our energy and life activities to obtain natural balance and health.

We all contain and express each of these elements in different measures, depending on our energetic structure and our condition or stages of change.

The creative and control cycles are an expression of the natural balance of energy in the universe. When our energy is out of balance these cycles may be distorted. We can use the wisdom they give us to re-establish equilibrium on all levels of our being.

THE CREATIVE OR SUPPORTING CYCLE – is where one element creates or supports another element but the element being supported also has the potential to be over-demanding on the element doing the supporting. This is why it is sometimes referred to as the "Mother and Child Cycle".

Water nourishes wood. Wood fuels the fire. Fire burns to create ash that forms the soil. Soil produces the minerals of metal, which dissolves its minerals into water.

When we need to work on an element, which needs emphasis, we can either choose to work directly on that element or use the one that supports or creates it.

THE CONTROL CYCLE – is where one element has the power to control or override another.

Water can dampen down a raging fire. Fire can melt the coldness of metal. Metal can cut wood down to size. Wood can cover and put its roots into the earth. Earth contains water and prevents it overflowing.

We can use this cycle to control an overactive element or see the potential an overcharged element has to override a weakened one.

Understanding these simple fundamental principles in nature can help us to regain harmony and balance in every area of our lives.

Watch nature at work giving the elements out in the right quantities:
For example: It provides moisture so fruit will grow, but too much and the
fruit will rot. The solutions to so many of life's problems lie in striking the
right balance. Your problems will resolve themselves when you know how to
adjust, measure and apportion the elements properly, like nature. Then all
around you there will be an abundance of the fruits of life including joy,
happiness and harmony.

Omraam Aivanhov

THE FIVE TRANSFORMATIONS IN NATURE

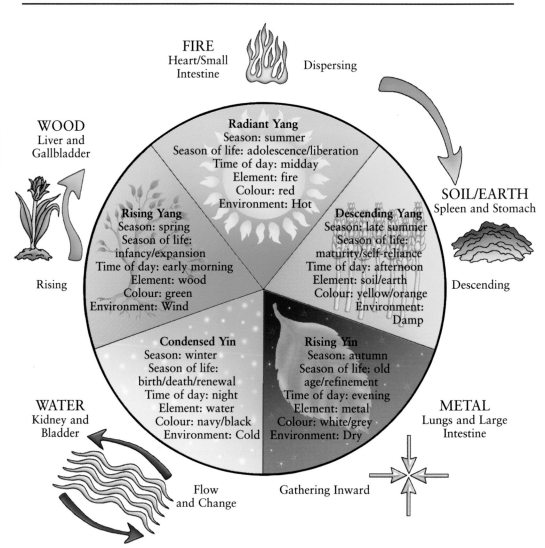

MIND, BODY AND EMOTIONS

FIRE
Primary organs: heart and
small intestine
Secondary organs: Pericardium
and Triple Heater

Dispersing

WOOD
liver and
gallbladder

SOIL/EARTH
spleen and stomach

Governs: circulation,
emotions, blood vessels
Energy: conversion/assimilation
Sense: speech (tongue)
Voice: laughing, high pitch
Emotions: highs and *lows*, joy and
love *(or a lack of)*
Mental: spiritual awareness,
inspiration

Governs:
muscles,
joints
Energy: distri-
bution/storage, sexual
vigour (male),
Sense: sight
Voice: shouting, clipped
Emotions: *angry, impatient,*
humorous, gentle
Mental: flexibility, freedom, vision,
creativity

Governs:
lymphatic,
immune and
digestive systems,
reproduction (female)
Sense: taste
Voice: sing-song
Energy: ingestion/digestion
Emotions: *worried, low in self-
esteem and sense of self-worth,*
caring, supportive
Mental: ideas/opinions and
concentration

Rising

Descending

Governs:
bones, skeleton,
hormones/reproduction
systems, adrenal glands, libido
Energy: purification/regulation
Sense: hearing (ears)
Voice: trembling, groaning
Emotions: *anxious, insecure,
lacks direction,* courageous,
secure, determined
Mental: memory,
ambition, will-power

Governs:
respiration, skin,
elimination
Sense: smell (nose)
Voice: weepy, breathy
Energy: exchange/elimination
Emotions: *can't let go, grieving,
insular,* positive, open,
enthusiastic
Mental: leadership, clarity,
intuition strength

WATER
kidney and
bladder

METAL
lungs and large
intestine

Flow
and Change

Gathering Inward

Note: there are positive and negative emotions on this chart. The
negative emotions are indicated in *italic*.

PHASES OF ENERGY – THE CREATING CYCLE

Five Seasonal Cycle

- *Corresponding colour*
- *Corresponding element*
- *Corresponding hours of the day*
- *Corresponding meridians/organ partnerships*

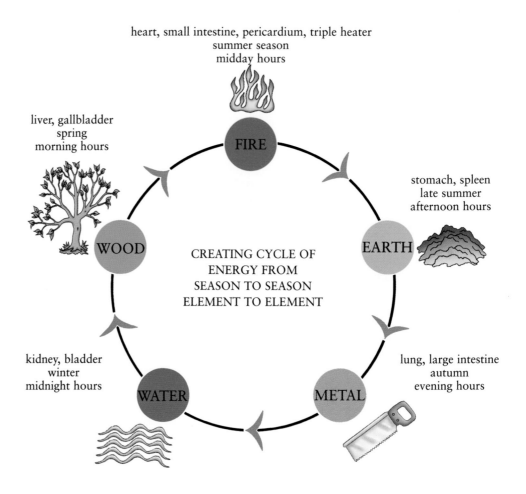

- **WATER** *feeds* **WOOD**
- **WOOD** *fuels* **FIRE**
- *The ashes from* **FIRE**, *feed and nourish the* **EARTH**
- **EARTH** *supplies* **METALS** (**MINERALS**)
- **METALS** (**MINERALS**) *are carried by* **WATER**

THE CONTROLLING CYCLE

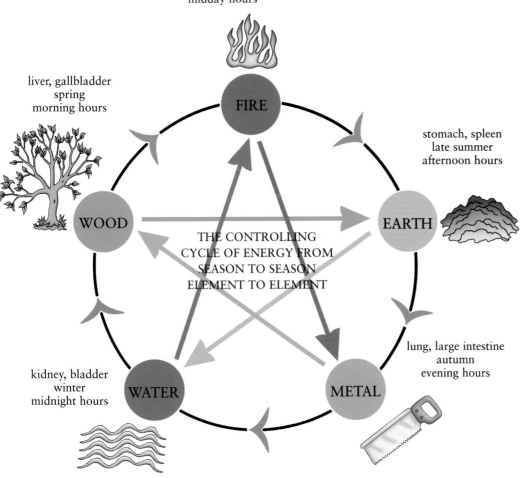

heart, small intestine, pericardium, triple heater
summer season
midday hours

liver, gallbladder
spring
morning hours

stomach, spleen
late summer
afternoon hours

FIRE

WOOD

EARTH

THE CONTROLLING
CYCLE OF ENERGY FROM
SEASON TO SEASON
ELEMENT TO ELEMENT

lung, large intestine
autumn
evening hours

kidney, bladder
winter
midnight hours

WATER

METAL

- *WATER puts out FIRE*
- *FIRE melts METAL*
- *METAL cuts WOOD*
- *WOOD sustains the EARTH*
- *EARTH contains WATER*

CONSTITUTION AND CONDITION

"Health is governed by natural laws. To restore it you simply rectify the imbalance and create a suitable environment so healing naturally takes place."

CONSTITUTION

Our constitution relates to the capacity and potential we are born with. It is formed by hereditary factors from our parents and ancestors, the mental and physical influences of the mother during pregnancy and the nourishment through food and the environment during gestation and early growth. This manifests in our structure, which is unlikely to change during the course of our lives.

Right: our constitution is formed through food and the environment during gestation and early growth.

Examples of influences:

	FATHER'S INFLUENCE	**MOTHER'S INFLUENCE**
Sex of child	Sperm active: female child more likely	Egg active: a male child more likely
Major systems	Nervous and respiratory	Digestive, circulatory and reproductive
Face and body	Left side	Right side
Mental and physical	Intellectual, social, ideological	Physical, sensory, emotional

Foods if eaten to excess during
pregnancy and the growing period
also have certain influences:

KINDS OF FOOD EATEN	MENTAL TENDENCIES	PHYSICAL TENDENCIES
Fruit and nuts	Sentimentality/sensitivity	Weaker digestive function
Dairy food	Gentle/slow/dull responses	Skin problems, formation of mucus, heart/circulatory disorders
Stimulants and spices	Emotional insecurity, irritability	Heart/circulatory disorders, high blood pressure
Meat, poultry, eggs	Determination/materialism/ stubbornness	Heart/circulatory disorders
Sugar and sweets	Nervousness, illusion	Obesity, diabetes, skin diseases, kidney and excretory disorders

*Below: our consti-
tution is reflected in
our face.*

The main areas on the face that
relate to our constitution are
the size and shape of our head,
ears, teeth and eyebrows (see
individual sections)

	YIN	YANG
Size of head to body average is 1:7	Smaller head to body	Larger head to body
Shape of face	Thin, narrow Oval Triangular with small chin	Square Round Triangular with wider jaw
Bones, hands, feet	Taller, thinner, fine	Shorter, stockier, bigger bones
Attributes	Delicate, intellectual, changeable	Practical, steady, powerful, robust
Behaviour	Artistic, intuitive	Pragmatic, steady
Teeth	Smaller, closer	Larger, with gaps

By being able to define our unique constitution we are better able to understand where our potential strengths and weaknesses lie. These are regarded as neither good nor bad, but more an aid to understanding who we are constitutionally. This knowledge can help us to take advantage of this potential and use it to make creative choices in our lives.

THE RELATIONSHIP OF FACE TO BODY

The microcosm represents the macrocosm in oriental diagnosis. The head is always regarded as a microcosm of the body itself, so you can project the entire body on to the face.

Each of us has a differently proportioned body or head, depending on the foods we are nourished with whilst we are in our mother's womb. The sections of the face, which develop concurrently with the functions of the body, reflect the constitutional quality of the primary systems.

Equally proportioned sections indicate balanced activity between the systems. If one section appears larger or more defined, it generally tells us that this area of activity and expression is a more dominant trait. Clearly accentuated and structured sections show inherent strengths, while vague, loose or immature qualities imply weakness.

HOW THE FACE IS MADE

Facial proportions tell us a great deal about a person's constitution and condition at birth.

Days 1–28 – the fertilised egg travels down the fallopian tube towards the depth of the womb where implantation occurs and the organism rapidly increases in size for the next 21 days. These days account for the main development of the top of the face. Birthmarks may occur at this time.

Days 21–63 – the middle section of the face is formed

Days 63–189 – the bottom section of the face is formed, with an increasing proportion of 1:3

The three systems develop continuously but the principle development for each system takes place as follows:

- *first three months: nervous system – correspondingly the intellectual nature*

- *second three months: the circulatory and excretory/respiratory systems – emotional nature*

- *final three months: the digestive/reproductive systems – the strength of will.*

Below: the development of the face.

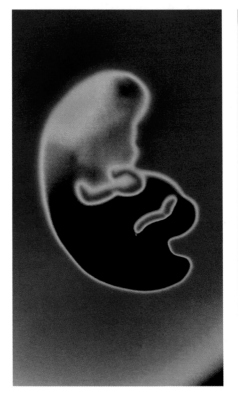 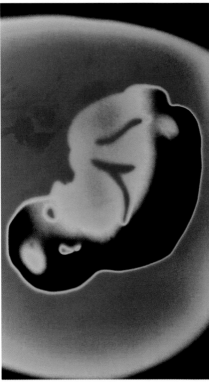 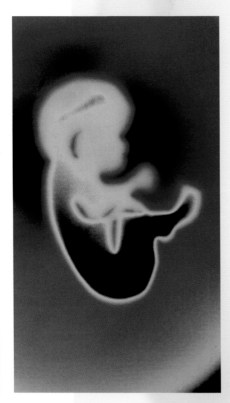

CONDITION

Our condition, however, is a different matter altogether and is well within our scope for change. It can be a constant mode of change from active to passive, tired to energetic, happy to sad, overweight or underweight.

This change is dependent on primary factors such as food, exercise, environment, lifestyle and relationships. Indications can be seen more obviously in the muscles, skin and the periphery of the body. By understanding the various factors that support our condition we can begin to deal with any extremes that may be upsetting our equilibrium.

Take, for example, an oak rocking chair. Its basic design, structure and the material it is made of is its constitution. This is unlikely to change during its lifetime (it cannot suddenly shrink and become a pine dining chair without arms). However, its condition may change many times depending on who owns it and how it is taken care of. If it is looked after, waxed and kept in the right environment, it will beautify with age. Or it may become dented or damaged, depending on the wear and tear it is subjected to. A wood such as oak will sustain more hard knocks whereas pine is more easily damaged.

NERVOUS SYSTEM
AND
RELATED TENDENCIES

CIRCULATORY, EXCRETORY AND RESPIRATORY SYSTEMS
AND RELATED TENDENCIES

DIGESTIVE AND REPRODUCTIVE
SYSTEMS AND
RELATED TENDENCIES

THE ORIENTAL APPROACH TO DIET

For thousands of years, oriental doctors considered our daily diet to be the basic tool with which to approach any health problem before using herbs, acupuncture, homeopathic preparations or more conventional approaches. The food eaten during your time in the womb forms the basis of your shape and constitution, just as the food eaten after birth plays a major role in your condition, health, energy levels and sense of well-being.

The secret of our daily diet is finding balance and the correct fuel that is suitable for our constitution, condition, activity and lifestyle.

Our chi (energy) and blood are nourished by our daily food, and certain foods and flavours are used to stimulate and strengthen certain organs or systems. Specific foods are used to prevent or even remedy specific illnesses, as they dramatically effect our internal environment (see self-help section). The expense and side effects of drugs have caused many people to re-evaluate this traditional oriental approach.

but differ in their structures. Traditional doctors discovered that the structure of foods has a beneficial effect on the parts of the body with a similar structure – for example, the walnut is a similar structure to the brain and acts as a brain tonic. The cauliflower is good for the lungs as its construction is the same. If someone needed to strengthen their kidneys they were given kidney to eat.

Modern medicine's approach to medication is very analytical. For example, if a certain mushroom has traditionally been used to lower a fever, the manufacturer will identify the active chemical ingredient (yang) then extract it and reproduce it in tablet form, discarding some of the nutritional ingredients of the whole plant. The yin aspect, which although not active just by its presence can have a protective or supporting role for the yang.

Another example is that foods may have the same chemical ingredients

Below: the cauliflower is good for the lungs as its construction is the same.

THE RIGHT SEASON AND THE RIGHT FUEL

Eating food in the appropriate season and food that is grown locally to where you live gives you the right energy and internal temperature to remain healthy. If you fed an Eskimo on a diet of mangos, he would suffer from cold inside and become sick, as mangos are grown in a tropical climate and serve to cool the body down. A high-fat food would serve to heat the body and keep it warm.

The amount of energy we get from our food is being seriously depleted by additives, pesticides, refrigeration and the quality of soil that it is grown in.

In Japan, the body is thought of as a fire mass and can only continue to exist if the fuel is added from time to time, This fuel we call food and drink. We also need oxygen to make the transformation of food into energy complete.

- *We can choose a quick burning or slow burning fuel. If you consume slow burning fuel such as meat then you need to eat less often.*

- *Certain foods like vegetables need to be eaten in larger quantities, whereas other foods such as fats are eaten in smaller amounts to give the same amount of energy.*

- *Some foods are more clean-burning fuels and other highly refined foods give off fumes, which cloud perception or fog our minds and stop clear thinking.*

- *Some foods can be stored, whereas others decay or rot easily. So if certain foods are allowed to remain in the intestines, they can cause stagnation and fermentation. An example of this is eating fruit after a large meal which causes it to ferment, so it is best to eat fruit between meals and not on a full stomach.*

- *By drinking too much at mealtimes or eating too much (especially cold or raw food), we can literally put out the digestive fire or wash away our digestive juices*

- *The fire of our digestive process also needs oxygen to revive it. Breathing is the quickest way to restore energy and health as you can live without food for up 30 days, without drink for 6 days, but without oxygen for only 3 minutes.*

The macrobiotic philosophy (a word translated from the writings of Hippocrates, the father of Western medicine – *macro* meaning large/great, *bios* meaning life) teaches us that a wholesome balanced diet is the most direct path to good health and longevity. It emphasises the importance of where we live (climate and location), what we do (activity levels) and our present state of health (physiology), in order to assess our individual nutritional needs. In Japan in the 19th century, they understood the yin and yang quality of foods and the effect it has in creating balance on every level.

Yang (heaven's force) produces yang foods such as root vegetables that grow down into the soil (yin) and which, like salt, have a more contracting effect on the body.

Then the yin energy (earth's force) produces foods that grow up out of the earth and have a more cooling and expansive effect on the body.

The Chinese also understand the importance of food energetics. In the West we describe food as having certain amounts of protein, fats, minerals and vitamins. In the East, food is described as having certain qualities such as warming or cooling including the action that certain flavours have on the organs. They take into account the methods and length of cooking times. For example, raw or faster-cooked food is more cooling and is best eaten in summer, whereas in winter we need more warming foods cooked for longer periods.

Refer to the chart Food and the Five Tastes on page 85.

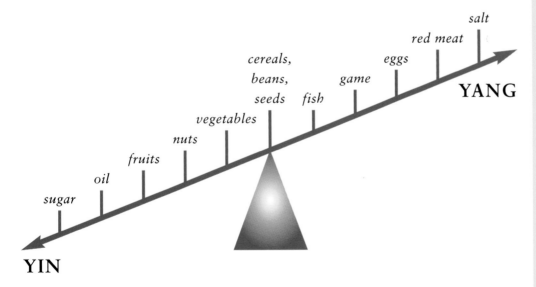

salt

red meat

eggs

cereals,
beans,
seeds   game

vegetables   fish

nuts

fruits

oil

sugar

YANG

YIN

LOOKING DEEPER AND SEEING FURTHER
How to unravel the mystery of the facial body map

During the foetal period, the navel functioned as the centre of the entire body structure. We grew from here, which explains why in the oriental healing arts this area is considered to be the seat of our wisdom and intuition and the place on which all movements should be centred. After our birth this centre shifts to the mouth, explaining the correlation of head and body.

Our head becomes the upper sphere and our body the lower sphere. Our face is our outer expression, revealing the condition of our inner self. Our mouth represents the digestive system as a whole and our nose represents the spine. The middle of the face corresponds to the middle organs and our forehead corresponds to the lower part of the body. Areas of our face relate to the condition of the different organs and their functions in our body.

- *THE MOUTH as a whole shows the condition of our entire digestive system. More specifically, the upper lip shows the condition of our stomach, the lower lip our intestines and the area below the lower lip our large intestine. The mouth corners show the condition of our duodenum(see section on lips).*

- *THE AREA AROUND THE MOUTH represents our sexual organs and their functions. In the case of women the philtrum indicates the uterus and the corners of the mouth the strength of the ovaries. In men the area under the centre of the lower lip is associated with the prostate.*

- *THE NOSE in general represents our spine. More specifically, the tip represents our heart and its functions, the nostrils and cheeks our lungs and beside the nostrils our bronchi. The middle part of the nose represents our stomach. The top part of the nose reveals the health of the pancreas and the side of the nose and inner corner of the eye the spleen.*

- *THE EYES – the left eye represents our spleen and pancreas while the right eye represents our liver and gallbladder*

- *BETWEEN THE EYEBROWS gives an indication of the condition of our liver, and the temples our spleen.*

- *THE EARS represent our kidneys, left and right respectively.*

- *THE FOREHEAD as a whole indicates our intestines and the upper forehead our bladder.*

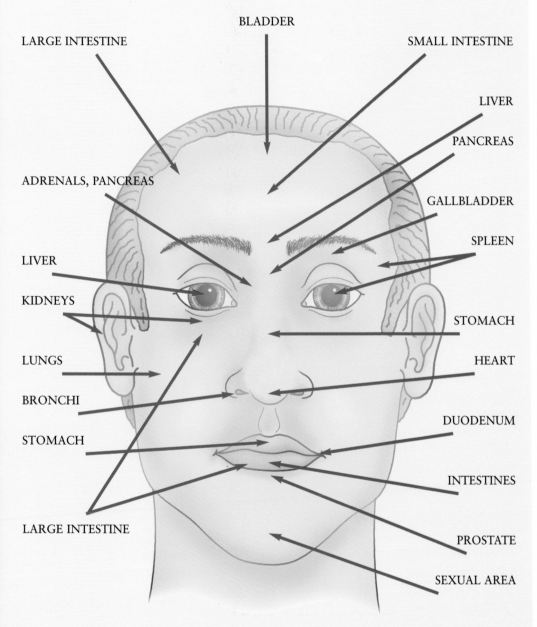

BLADDER

LARGE INTESTINE

SMALL INTESTINE

LIVER

PANCREAS

Left: our face is the outer expression, revealing the condition of our inner self.

ADRENALS, PANCREAS

GALLBLADDER

SPLEEN

LIVER

KIDNEYS

STOMACH

LUNGS

HEART

BRONCHI

DUODENUM

STOMACH

INTESTINES

LARGE INTESTINE

PROSTATE

SEXUAL AREA

Below are some examples of the indications we might find and some useful remedies. Refer to the self-help section for further ways to support the elements and organs concerned.

ORGAN AND ELEMENT RELATIONSHIP	FACIAL APPEARANCE AND EXPRESSION	INDICATIONS	REMEDIES
LUNGS AND BRONCHI (Metal element)	Sunken grey cheeks	Poor oxygenation and lack of facial expression	Breathing exercises Avoid smoking (support metal)
	Red swollen cheeks or puffiness	Mucus or internal heat or congestion in lungs	Avoid excess dairy, fatty foods and red meat
	Broken capillaries and sagging cheeks	Poor resilience of lungs and diaphragm	Breathing exercises, lots of fresh air. Avoid sugar, tropical fruits and baked flour products
	Open pores	Lack of essential mineral salts that may have been lost through sweat or stress	Increase fresh fruit and vegetables and cut down on stressful factors
LARGE INTESTINE (Metal element)	Swelling outside lower lip or lower lip appears dry, cracked or purple Puffiness on top of cheek bone	Expansion of intestines or irregular bowel movements, irritable bowel	Abdominal and breathing exercises Avoid yeast products, raw foods/cereals, overcooked mushy foods and fast eating. Chew well, finish projects, check for food intolerance

ORGAN AND ELEMENT RELATIONSHIP	FACIAL APPEARANCE AND EXPRESSION	INDICATIONS	REMEDIES
LARGE INTESTINE (Metal element)	Tightness of lower lip	Constipation	Avoid excess yang foods and salt, express emotions, massage abdomen, clear clutter at home
STOMACH (Earth element)	Swollen, cracked or red upper lip	Expanded or inflamed stomach, excess acidity	Chew well, avoid sugar and spices. Look at diet and avoid overworking/stress
	Yellow around lips or lips lacking tone	Overeating or chaotic eating, overworking or digestive weakness	Avoid extremes of yin and yang, eat regular meals in a relaxed way, perhaps consult a nutritionist
SPLEEN/LYMPH (Earth element)	Swelling of temples	Sluggishness, fatigue. A poor relationship with self	Avoid rich gourmet and sugary foods and overeating (support spleen)
	Hollow in temples	Lymph system low in energy	Gentle exercise to support system, avoid refined foods
PANCREAS (Earth element)	Horizontal lines across bridge of nose or bluish bruised appearance at inner corner of the eye	Sugar intolerance or excess protein, Lack of endurance, craving for sweets, irritable or overbearing	Avoid sugar, coffee, chocolate and rich foods refined carbohydrates and overeating. Eat little and often (support earth)

Organ and element relationship	Facial appearance and expression	Indications	Remedies
Heart (Fire element)	Red nose and face	Tendency for high blood pressure or internal heat	Cut down on animal food and slow pace of life down
	Purple nose	Low blood pressure or stagnation	Avoid sugar, coffee and alcohol. Take up yoga
Small Intestine (Fire element)	Swelling in central part of lips	Poor absorption	Avoid refined and processed foods and flour products and chew food well
	Horizontal lines and swelling in centre of forehead	Stagnation of mucus in intestines, difficulty separating pure from impure in all aspects of life (mind, body and emotions)	Avoid dairy food, mucus-producing foods and saturated fats. Mentally and emotionally change beliefs that are not serving you
Bladder (Water element)	Swelling or wetness of upper forehead	Organ weakness	Avoid excess liquids, especially soft drinks and wine, discover what is making you anxious and address
Kidney (Water element)	Swollen bags under eyes	Swollen kidneys and oedema	Avoid excess liquids, salt, mucus-producing foods and flour products. Do exercises for lower back, rub kidneys. Take up t'ai chi.

Organ and element relationship	Facial appearance and expression	Indications	Remedies
KIDNEY (Water element)	Ears that appear red	Stressing adrenal glands	Cut down on caffeine, stimulants and reduce stress factors
	Sudden increase in crow's feet at eye corners (specially in young)	Tired/overworked kidneys	Avoid excess liquids and alcohol
LIVER (Wood element)	Puffy and swollen, oily skin or rashes between eyebrows	Lack of consistent energy Loud voice	Avoid excess, greasy, oily, fatty foods, eggs, meat, alcohol, sugar
	Tightness and contraction with deep vertical lines between eyes	Impatient, workaholic, demanding on others and self, single minded and focused	Avoid excess salt, animal foods and alcohol. Chew well and slowly. Slow down, take time to relax and enjoy life
GALLBLADDER (Wood element)	Bags in upper inside corner of eye, bumpy or greasy along eyebrow ridge, yellow sclera or small hook-shaped lines between eyebrows	Organ clogged or under stress	Cut out dairy food, fried food and cold liquids and fats especially cheeses
SEXUAL ORGANS (For males see wood and females water and earth elements)	Spots, pimples or blotchy appearance, especially around the chin area.	Discharge from reproductive organs or yeast infection	Cut down on fermented foods or those containing yeast or sugar. Reduce mucus-producing foods especially peanuts

Right: the wood face.

THE WOOD TYPE

Rectangular in appearance longer than it is wide, the forehead is high and the cheeks are narrow. This type is both genial and dignified and is associated with being romantic, idealistic and optimistic. The possessor of the wood face is energetic and forward-thinking with leadership potential and has strong ideals and determination. They are strong leaders and organisers, and can shoulder a lot of responsibility.

They value challenge, contest and achievement but can fear authority, frustration and interference. They will stand for a point of principal and have a philosophical attitude towards life. When balanced, the face is kindly and benevolent but they can also demand things are done their own way and may sometimes express themselves in an arrogant manner. They mean well but can be tactless in imposing their views as they have strong convictions and can find it hard to compromise. Care must be taken that the strength of a positive and uplifting viewpoint does not lead to a desire to control. If they become ill, they can become indecisive, irritable and suffer from headaches. (Refer to self-help section for the wood element)

Their life challenges are:

- *to balance the need to be in charge with the companionship of equals*

- *to ensure that the desire to act and to do does not make them over-impulsive.*

- *to beware the fear of vulnerability and loss of control does not make them over-controlling.*

THE FIRE TYPE

This type has prominent cheekbones and pointed features like a triangle, which is the shape symbolic of fire, often with red hair or freckles. They tend to be emotional, articulate, tactile and communicative and their gaze can be somewhat daunting. The temperament of the fire person is sociable, excitable and ambitions, and they have a strong desire to burn brightly, seeking excitement. Their emotions tend to be somewhat extreme, which can lead to outbursts of anger if their plans are thwarted. They can be extremely persuasive and charming but the face can change easily if they lose control, which challenges relationships. They desire spontaneity, expression and excitement and fear inactivity, dullness, roughness and boundaries. If unwell, they can become withdrawn or lose motivation in life. (Refer to self-help section for the fire element)

Their life challenges are:

- *to balance contact and intimacy with time for solitude*

- *to temper the desire to please and say "yes" with the occasional "no"*

- *to balance the intensity of living in the moment with an awareness of what follows.*

Left: the fire face.

THE EARTH TYPE

This type is noticeably square with its height and width apparently the same, making the nose and mouth seem wide. They have a distinctive jaw line, which gives them an air of toughness and determination, although some would say stubbornness. Their energy is high, they are practical and reliable and they desire involvement, commitment and loyalty, but they have a tendency to immediately jump to conclusions before the facts are known. They impulsively get themselves into trouble without help from anyone else. They thrive on stability and permanence, but their temper and life can be unpredictable. They enjoy contact sports and an active family and social life, but can be prone to worry and digestive problems. (Refer to self-help section for the earth element)

Their life challenges are:

- *to live life to the full but not to get weighed down or overburdened*

- *to be needed or involved but not to lose their sense of self in the process*

- *to feel centred throughout the changing challenges of life.*

Right: the earth face.

Left: the metal face.

THE METAL TYPE

This face is oval and the eyes are large and lively, denoting intelligence and sharp perceptions. This type tend to live in their heads and are more the intellectual type than the manual labourer. Their mind is usually active and they have a hard working attitude but may have difficulty in letting go and relaxing. They like to debate issues as long as they are sure of their ground and are quite capable of clever word play and a dazzling display of pungent wit.

They value definition, quality, correctness, and precision and seek a high standard. Although they like meeting new people, they will keep all but a few at a distance because emotional closeness and intimacy is disturbing to them. They can be uncomfortable with spontaneity, vagueness, nonsense and chaos. They are good politicians and organisers and can be ambitious and cunning. They are good with finance as security is important to them. If they lose strength, they are prone to negative thinking, depression and respiratory and intestinal problems. (Refer to self-help section for the metal element)

Their life challenges are:

- *to enjoy relationships but keep their own space*

- *to know what is right and accept what is safe*

- *to aspire towards beauty and high ideals but settle for what is practical.*

THE WATER TYPE

This face is round, sometimes chubby, and often referred to as a moon face. It can be pale or drained of colour and the eyes, like the element, can be watery. This type are often wrongly accused of being lazy. They are generally quite and gentle by nature. They tend too work to hard and suffer from exhaustion and then become easily tired and lethargic, but they have an abundance of imagination and create a rich fantasy world, which they often find it easier to inhabit than the real one. Sometimes their vivid imagination can give rise to unrealistic expectations, disappointment and hypochondria. They desire solitude and time to conserve their resources. If they do not get these they can become dependent on others for support. They thrive on mystery, privacy and originality, but if they find themselves alone for too long they can put off decisions so it is good for them to set themselves goals. They fear superficiality, exposure, wastefulness and rashness. When unwell they can become easily stressed, suffer kidney infections or back problems. (Refer to the self-help section for the water element)

Their life challenges are:

- *to enjoy being alone but not feel abandoned*

- *to feel deep and connected without being absorbed or overwhelmed*

- *to discover the truth without overexposure.*

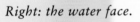

Right: the water face.

THE THREE ASPECTS OF THE FACE

In ancient times, the shape of the face was more predictable as people ate only the foods grown locally to where they lived. By eating more contracting foods in the winter and expanding foods in the summer, their face shapes developed according to the seasons. During the embryonic stage of life, the three systems develop continuously but the principal development of each system takes place as follows.

During the first three months the nervous system progresses rapidly. Then during the next three months the circulatory system develops, followed by the final stage which is the digestive system.

The key to oriental diagnosis is that the macrocosm can be seen in the microcosm.

As the brain develops so does the size of the forehead, so the forehead reflects the person's intellectual nature and nervous system.

The mid region between the eyes and mouth indicates the emotional nature and the circulatory and respiratory systems.

The chin and jaw, including the area below the nose and around the mouth, reflect the strength of the will and the digestive and reproductive systems.

Look and see if they are balanced, or whether one area dominates the face.

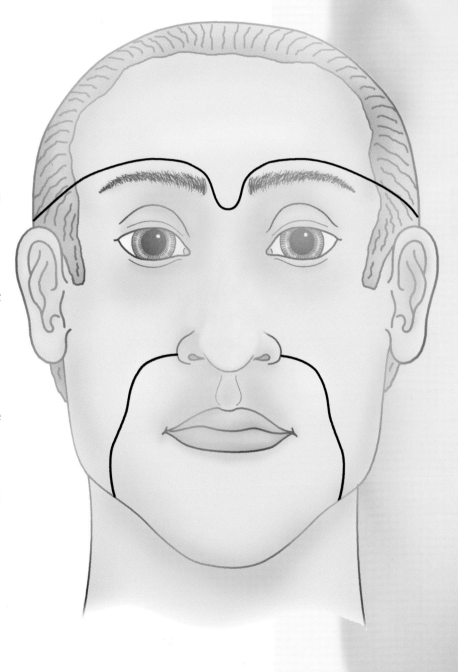

Below: the three aspects of the face.

THE BALANCED FACE

If the three areas are equal, the person has a balanced nature and is not dominated by mind, emotions or will. They attempt to make rational decisions based on harmony between the three aspects of their being.

Balanced features but a large round head indicates that the person has tremendous power, a rare blend of intellectual development, an understanding of the emotional needs of others, a strong will and the courage to bring their plans to fruition. They are farsighted, have good social judgment and possess huge powers of endurance – a good example was Sir Winston Churchill.

They can have a tendency to be arrogant so must identify strongly with the needs of others.

HIGH FOREHEAD AND SMALLER MID AND CHIN SECTION

This is the face of someone who is dominated by their high intellect and conceptual mind. They are great planners and abstract thinkers who can serve as advisers to powerful leaders. They must guard against being aloof, critical or cynical and avoid intrigues or struggles for power. They cannot endure the demands of leadership because the chin area shows their will is weak. They can possess visionary ideas, but need help from more practical and down-to-earth people to carry them through.

Below: high forehead and smaller mid and chin section

THE WELL-DEVELOPED MID-REGION

This person tends to be very emotional or even sentimental and they can sympathise with the pain of others. They understand the suffering of life and seek to heal it. They have a highly developed maternal or sensitive nature. They are often artistic and have a fine appreciation of beauty, especially in the more physical arts such as sculpture, dance and painting.

Their chief weakness is that they can be thrown about by their feelings. They are volatile and lively. They can fly off the handle one moment and then be placid the next, exploding with joy or plunging into a deep depression. They need to develop a sense of proportion and a more business-like and practical approach to life.

THE BIG JAW

These people have a powerful will and strong sense of purpose. They can endure conflict and remain focused on their objective. Such people are practical, goal-orientated and often workaholics, but they can be dominating. They have courage and tenacity and will fight till the battle is won. People with strong jaws can be materialistic and status conscious. They want it known that they possess the best of everything. They can be extremely willful and stubborn. They often ignore the ideas and feelings of others to follow their own course.

They bulldoze their way through things or pretend that opposition simply does not exist. They tend to see things in black and white and see others as either for or against them. For these people there is no middle road and they can become attached to personal goals, often to the exclusion of others' needs. They must work on developing compassion and human understanding so that they can share with others a greater appreciation of the deeper meaning of life.

Below: people with a big jaw have a powerful will and strong sense of purpose.

Left: a well developed mid-region indicates a person who is emotional or even sentimental.

READING EMOTIONS ON THE FACE

Below: the traditional healer treats the liver with diet, herbs, acupuncture and lifestyle re-balancing.

Many centuries ago oriental healers developed an understanding of our need to function as an integrated whole on all levels of our being and consequently balance our emotional, mental and physical health and strength. Emotional stability depends on the healthy functioning of the entire body including each individual organ. When a particular organ is stressed or depleted, the energy it gives out as it performs its function can become distorted. One of the signs of this condition manifests itself on the emotional level.

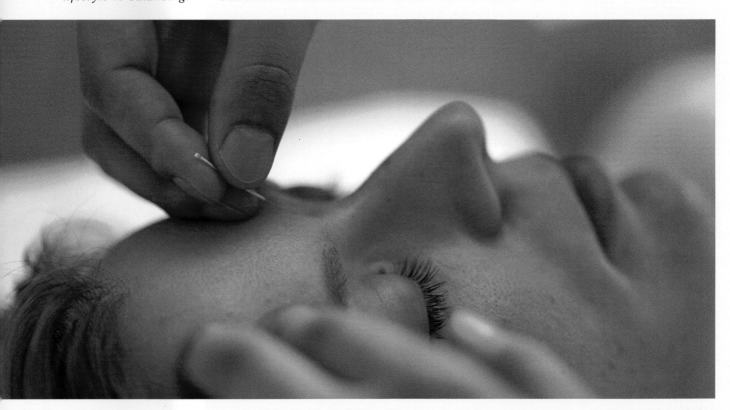

Likewise negative or repressed emotions repeatedly felt can affect the overall stability and health of particular organs and therefore our overall health. How we look after the physical body can directly effect the emotions we feel.

For example, if a person injures their liver by unhealthy eating and drinking, they may then suffer from acute or repressed anger and hostility, thus revealing the presence of an unbalanced liver. Rather than talk endlessly about a person's psychological condition, the traditional healer would treat the liver with diet, herbs, acupuncture and lifestyle re-balancing. Then the extremes of emotion would diminish, and equilibrium in the emotions and the organ would be restored.

The emotions associated with each element are as follows –

ELEMENT AND ORGANS	IMBALANCE	BALANCE
WOOD **LIVER/GALLBLADDER**	Angry, frustrated, volatile, abusive, argumentative, impatient, rigid thinking, revengeful, irritable, enraged, moody, depressed	Patient, humorous, gentle, kind, easy-going, good at planning, well organised, flexible thinker, creative, full of new ideas, motivated
FIRE **HEART/SMALL INTESTINE**	Extreme in emotions, shy, nervous laugh, hysterical, anxious, over-excited, sorrowful, lacking joy/love, changeable mind/moods, hurting, isolated	Joyful, calm, emotional stable, gregarious, communicative, sociable, secure, loving, generous, fun
EARTH **STOMACH/SPLEEN**	Cynical, self-pitying, suspicious, critical, cold in relationships, unfulfilled, needy, greedy, empty, filled with doubt or feeling deprived, worried	Understanding, compassionate, supportive, reliable, centred, content, confident, thoughtful, considerate
METAL **LUNG AND LARGE INTESTINE**	Prolonging grief, unable to let go, depressed, indifferent, intolerant, regretful, sad, feeling guilty, withdrawn, negative, apathetic, insular	Positive, open, enthusiastic, emotionally stable, clear-minded, good at leadership, intuitive, possessing inner strength, modest, tolerant
WATER **KIDNEY/BLADDER**	Insecure, fearful, anxious, full of dread, panicky, inadequate, timid, reckless, paranoid, careless, sexually insecure, lacking willpower, stressed, restless, defensive	Courageous, strong-willed, vital, possessing a sense of inner direction, secure, relaxed, deep, reflective, determined, possessing a sense of inner power.

We have 57 facial muscles that express our changing condition and emotional tendencies very accurately. These muscles have a great deal of influence on our facial features. We are unconsciously reading these all the time to gain an impression of a person's energy and emotional state.

Below: our facial muscles greatly influence our facial features.

Therefore, personality, energy levels and emotional character-istics influence how your face looks and also reveal the state of health of your internal organs. In the same way our hereditary and constitutional factors influence our facial features and bone structure.

How can you use this information?
If you are continually or regularly feeling a certain emotion, an imbalance in the organ or element related to it is indicated. Focus the mind and intention on the opposite and balancing emotion and use the charts in the self-help section to support and balance the organ and element concerned.

You can't control the beauty of the face but you can choose the expression on it,

You can't control life's difficult moments but you can choose how you respond to them,

You can't control a negative atmosphere around you but you can choose the atmosphere of your mind.

Bob Gass

The shape and profile view of the forehead can tell us much about the way a person thinks, their personality, what stresses them and how best to deal with their needs and challenges:

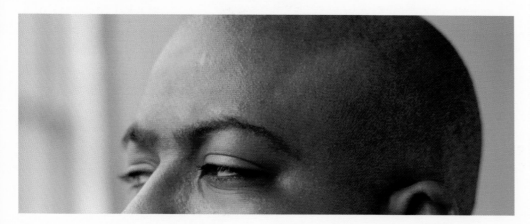

Below: the vertical forehead.

1. THE VERTICAL FOREHEAD
(vertical from brow to hairline)
Indicates a thinker who is very thorough and likes to have detailed information to understand fully. They need time to process information and will often retain this in great depth. They work better in an unhurried atmosphere with a structure or schedule. Give them time to question for clarification and to process information step by step.

Stress factor for them is having to skim through information without enough depth or detail and not having time to think things through. Under stress they can seem overwhelmed and confused or go into overload unable to retain any more information.

Creating their balance – they can practise summarising things.

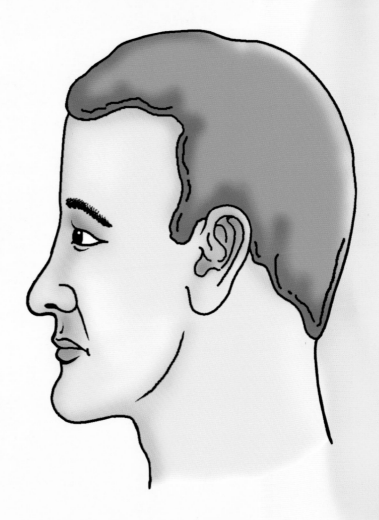

2. THE SLOPING FOREHEAD
(slopes back from brow to hairline)

With this type you need to keep your conversations straight to the point and, when discussing concepts, give them broad outlines, keeping it brief. They often come to conclusions or reach decisions very quickly.

Below: the sloping forehead.

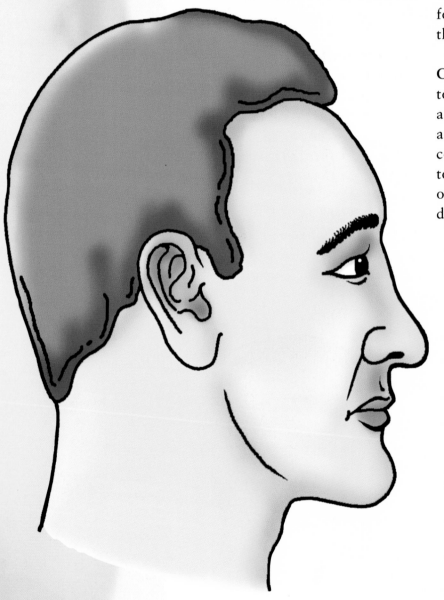

Stress factor for them is side-tracking, unnecessary chit chat or giving details without the bottom line. Speaking too slowly with pauses can annoy them and when bored they will either fidget, switch off or jump to finish conversations.

The greater the angle of the forehead the faster the thinker they are.

Creating their balance – they need to practise doing things involving a more detailed approach and avoid rushing things or jumping to conclusions too quickly. They need to develop a respect for the way others do things, including a difference of pace.

3. RIDGE ABOVE THE EYEBROWS

This person likes to have an order, structure or routine to work with, which they stick to quite unconsciously sometimes, but which gives them security and control. They enjoy being methodical and meticulous and like creating systems, often doing things the same way each day.

Stress factor for them is a lack of order or structure, being told to go with the flow, or being short of time to complete all the tasks in a set order. If they are forced into changes without consideration for their way of doing things, they can become defensive in justification of their system or act with stubbornness.

Creating their balance – to practise being more adaptable and spontaneous and avoid imposing routines on others.

4. GENTLY SHAPED FOREHEAD WITH NO RIDGE

This person likes to go with the flow and works best when doing things their own way. They like to be spontaneous and have a relaxed routine, with the minimum of order and structure. They can seem disorganised but have their own style of getting things done, although they can run out of time and be late for things.

Stress factor for them is being forced to stick to a rigid schedule or structure with no allowance for spontaneity and freedom, so they feel trapped and stifled. This will either cause them to rebel or use excuses to get out of these situations.

Creating their balance – to practise time management and how to do things in a more orderly way.

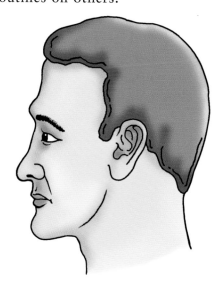 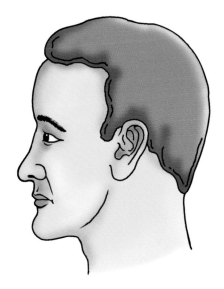

Far left: forehead ridged above the eyebrows.

Left: gently shaped forehead with no ridge.

LINES ON THE FOREHEAD

Everyone has lines on the forehead and in the oriental tradition they are thought to be of great significance. The forehead is directly in front of the forebrain so it reflects the nervous system. For example, chaotic lines on the forehead can indicate chaotic brain activity. In the East, meditation and chanting as a way of restoring mental calm and clarity of thought has long been valued.

The normal pattern is to have three lines that ideally should be straight, distinct and unbroken.

Top line = spiritual line – this represents our highest ideals and more spiritual nature.

Middle line = personality line – this represents our human personality and the strength or weakness of our ego.

Lower line = earth line – this represents our capacity for earthly matters such as work, finance and the ability to realise our ideas.

When all three lines are distinct, unbroken and strong – this indicates the person possesses a balanced view of themselves in relationship to their spiritual nature, ego and earthly roles and has an integrated personality that leads to good health and sound judgments. If they continue to take care of their health, they are likely to do well in life and succeed.

When there are many unbroken lines – this indicates a person with many interests, which in the extreme could lead to inconsistency in their life.

Breaks in any of the lines – indicate a problem or conflict in the corresponding aspect of life, so the person will have to work harder to gain mastery of this area. They often show where a person tends to focus in their life, and how compelled they may be to accomplish something in this area, which requires greater effort and more attention than the other aspects.

Right: in the oriental tradition lines on the forehead are of great significance.

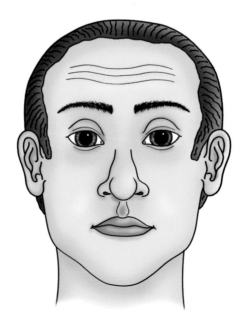

A broken earth line – indicates that the person needs to take good care of material matters and maintain a steady income and an orderly work schedule. They need to consciously develop good habits to sustain security in this unpredictable world, yet avoid overworking or becoming obsessive.

Broken earth line with strong personality and spiritual line – indicates that the person is working to realise an idealistic goal or vision.

Many broken lines – indicate an unreliable personality or changing health conditions. Care and attention is needed in order to sustain good health.

"Flying bird" broken lines (causing little pouches in the forehead) – indicate a more extreme personality who is continually changing or who has unstable health.

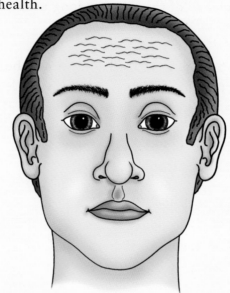

Left: forehead with "flying bird" lines.

Wavy lines – can indicate changes in health or unbalanced thinking. The person may find it hard to make up their mind or stick to a particular path. They may tend to change direction, job or partners more often than most people, or just always be wondering if the grass is greener on the other side.

The forehead is also related to the condition of the small intestine that governs the absorption of nourishment from food, thoughts and information. Wavy, troubled lines can indicate the person is finding it hard to separate the pure from the impure in the form of thoughts and information.

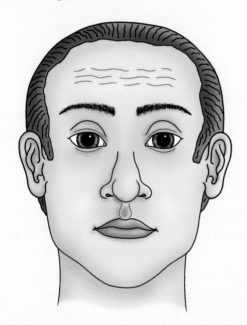

Left: forehead with many broken lines.

A missing line can reveal either of two things:

Firstly an absent line can mean that the person has the misconception that this aspect of their life is unimportant or irrelevant to their existence.

Secondly it can indicate the opposite – a very deep concern for that aspect, as if searching for something missing. The person goes to great lengths to discover more, or even become obsessed, about it.

Right: a forehead with one strong line.

A strong unbroken top line and middle line but missing bottom line indicates a solid sense of self. An emotionally balanced and idealistic person, but one who may be unbalanced concerning practical earthly matters, especially regarding finance and business. They may have trouble manifesting their high ideals in the material world. If they are to change the world for the better and find success, they need to understand that practical and economic lessons are spiritual lessons too.

A strong personality and earth line indicates the person has a strong sense of self with potential for leadership, but their materialistic goals are not necessarily balanced by spiritual ideals. They may consider these spiritual ideals to be ambiguous or unnecessary and avoid them. They may turn their attention instead to their career, material concerns or personal ambitions.

One strong line can indicate the person has a strong sense of that area but be orientated to seeking the others. It can also indicate steady health and consistent energy for life.

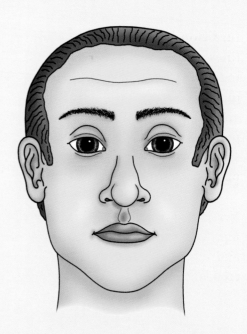

A single personality line without other lines can indicate a strong sense of self. One who can be powerful and admired, but in danger of becoming egotistical, superior or using others for personal advancement. They tend to be leaders, have charisma and can motivate others towards a single goal.

A single spiritual line indicates a highly idealistic but impractical person who must work at developing their own personality, sense of self and understanding of earthly matters.

A single earth line suggests the person sees life largely in terms of their material security and regards matters of the spirit as highly abstract and irrelevant to daily life.

Intuition lines are two horizontal lines above each eyebrow which indicate strong intuition and sound judgment when assessing others, and high spiritual ideals. This person has worked hard to make significant progress on their life path.

Vertical lines are an indication of intellect, someone who thinks a lot and who may be cautious or critical.

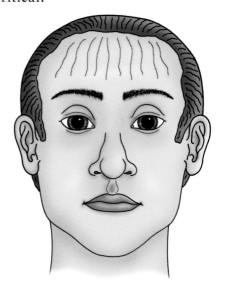

Vertical and horizontal lines indicate extreme intelligence, sensitivity and possibly nervousness.

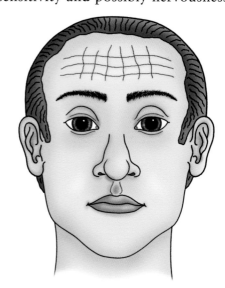

Deep vertical lines between the eyebrows indicate tension, stress, anger and nervousness.

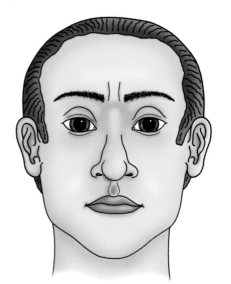

As a feature of the face we can now read the forehead to give us insight into a person's state of mind, mental focus and characteristics.

Left: Forehead with vertical and horizontal lines.

Left: Forehead with deep vertical lines.

Far left: Forehead with vertical lines.

THE EYES – "THE WINDOWS OF THE SOUL"

The eyes are the most expressive instruments in the human body. They reveal mental, physical and spiritual changes and also clearly indicate our constitution and attitudes.

Right: eyes are directly connected to the brain via the optic nerve.

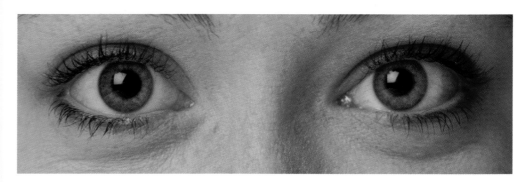

- *Eyes tell you 60 per cent of a person's current mental condition including the health of the nervous system connecting to every organ of the body. They are directly connected to the brain via the optic nerve. When the nervous system or brain is injured or damaged, the eyes lose their clarity or alertness.*

- *On a physiological level, brain cells require 30 times more oxygen than other cells and eye cells require eight times more. If there is a decrease in oxygen to the brain affecting mental alertness, the eyes will soon reflect this by becoming heavy, as they are also highly sensitive to oxygen depletion.*

- *In oriental medicine, it is a function of each of the major organs to govern one of our senses (refer to the Five Elements chart). The healthiness of our sight is regulated by the function of the liver. Spending too long looking at VDU screens, watching television or playing video games can over-tax and deplete the liver's energy, affecting its digesting and detoxifying functions. Red eyes can indicate heat in the liver*

- *In both Western and Eastern cultures, the eyes are said to be the window of the soul.*

- *In the East the brightness in someone's eyes relates to their mind and the sparkle in their eyes shows a good spirit (shen).*

THE SIZE OF EYES

Large eyes indicate a yin constitution suggesting that more yin foods were eaten during pregnancy and early childhood, making the person mentally sensitive, intuitive, emotional, delicate and gentle in character. They can be adversely affected by a lot of stress but overall they tend to have a wider view of things and see the whole picture.

Abnormally large eyes indicate nervous disorders, extreme sensitivity, nervousness, timidity and lack of confidence.

Small eyes indicate a more yang constitution and that more yang food was eaten at the time of pregnancy and during childhood. These are people who have a down-to-earth attitude to detail and who are good with figures and statistics. They tend to be determined and possess endurance, self-confidence and physical strength.

Abnormally small eyes can indicate a sharp or aggressive character.

Round eyes are more yin (feminine) indicating a more soft, sensitive, artistic and feminine quality, which can be the case for a man or woman.

Thin eyes are more yang (masculine) so for men it is a sign of an active strong constitution and for women a more physical, active and masculine approach to life.

Left: people with large eyes are mentally sensitive, intuitive, emotional, delicate and gentle in character.

Right: a wide distance between the eyes indicates a slow and gentle character, one who is more "laid back" and who could be indecisive or lack vitality.

DISTANCE BETWEEN THE EYES

In the early stage of foetal development the eyes are at the sides of the head like a fish. A strong contracting force draws the face together; if there is not enough of this force or too much it will affect the space between the eyes.

A shorter distance between the eyes indicates an intellectually and emotionally sharp character who can be aggressive, narrow-minded and stubborn. A lot of yang-quality foods were eaten during the gestation period and early life causing contraction, so there is a potential for the organs in the middle region of the body such as liver, pancreas, spleen and kidneys to be adversely affected if there is an excessive intake of fats, animal foods and salt later in life.

A wide distance between the eyes indicates a slow and gentle character, one who is more "laid back" and who could be indecisive or lack vitality. They can have a tendency towards isolation or separation in life.

A lot of yin foods were eaten during gestation and childhood so that the middle organs can be adversely affected by excessive consumption of yin-quality foods – these include sugars, soft drinks, tropical fruits and aromatic or stimulant food and beverages.

THE ANGLE OF THE EYES

Eyes that slant upward at the outer edges indicate a clear emotional and intellectual character. The greater the slope is, the greater the ambition. An extreme slope can indicate evil or megalomania as depicted in many cartoon characters, for example Cruella DeVille

Eyes that slope downwards at the outer edges indicate a more timid, gentle and accepting character. This person does not push situations, tends to avoid struggle and takes the path of least resistance.

A balanced angle means the person is diplomatic and a good negotiator.

WHAT THE EYES TELL US ABOUT OUR CONDITION

Vertical lines between eyebrows – most people have two light lines but if the lines are deep, the liver is troubled or congested and they may have bouts of anger or irritability.

Three lines can indicate much frustration and anger from an inappropriate diet or alcohol. **Three deep lines** suggest the person is becoming excessively single-minded or goal-orientated and they need to slow down and balance life with more yin activities. (Refer to the self-help section.) **A single deep line** indicates strong will or possibly a mid-life crisis. **Smaller hook-shaped lines** can indicate the gallbladder is under stress.

Left: eyes that slant upward at the outer edges indicate a clear emotional and intellectual character.

Eyelids relate to the gallbladder, so swelling or redness here could indicate heat in the gallbladder. This tells us to cut down on fats and alcohol and other heat producing foods.

A single tight and straight lid indicates mental clarity and a more yang-type person.

A double or loose lid indicates less physical strength and a more yin-type person.

Eye lashes when curving in can mean abnormality in reproductive function. In women this can mean menstrual cramps or lack of menstruation. This comes from eating too much salt, meat, eggs, fish and poultry without enough vegetables and grains to balance them.

Heaviness in the eyes with dull listless responses – indicates large intestine problems, overeating and lack of order in eating.

Bulging eyes show a slow metabolism. Check out the thyroid gland and the mineral balance in the body.

BLINKING

Children blink less often than adults as their condition is more yang, strong and active. A healthy adult blinks 3–4 times per minute, but can go without blinking for several minutes.

Less than 3–4 times suggests a more active person, sharp in both physical and mental character. If you are negotiating and your antagonist blinks less than you do, it is best to retreat, as you will lose.

Dogs and cats blink more than humans so if you stare at a tiger he will try to stare back but will finally back down.

Blinking more than 3–4 times can indicate excess consumption of yin-type foods so cut down on sugar, soft drinks, tea and coffee. Abnormally frequent blinking is a sign of extreme sensitivity, fear, timidity or irritability.

WHAT THE MOVEMENT OF THE EYE CAN TELL US

Someone who "holds your eye" with his or her own eyes while speaking to you is said to be trustworthy and honest.

The person with eyes that look up and down whilst speaking to you tends to be calculating things at the same times – a person who is shrewd, possibly scheming, and practical but cannot be relied upon.

Watery eyes tend to indicate a powerful sexual nature or flirtatiousness.

Round staring eyes denote a hard worker but someone who can have misfortune and has to be careful that plans don't go wrong. The "startled rabbit" look tends to indicate a kidney imbalance and denotes fear or anxiousness.

"Sanpaku" (Japanese) or "Three Whites" (Chinese)

This is where the eyeball takes an abnormally high or low position.

A balanced position indicates a balanced nervous system and a balanced view of life.

Upper Sanpaku – (Yang Sanpaku) – "The Three White Eye" is when the eyeballs are contracted and the iris floats downward so there is white above the eye and to the sides. This is normal in infants and young children. If this condition continues beyond early childhood, it is said to denote a personality that is determined, truthful, extremely confident, forthright but one who can be tactless. This person is extremely frustrated by the slow actions and apparent inefficiency of others and this can lead to outbursts of foul temper.

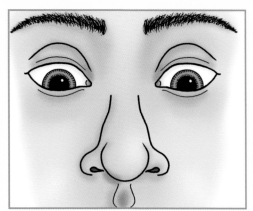

If this becomes extreme, it can be an indication of abnormal mentality and behaviour, including aggressiveness, violence and uncontrollable passions filled with rage. Such a person can become a danger to themselves or others and may even destroy themselves and take others with them. (Avoid extremely yang foods and balance wood energy.)

Lower Sanpaku – (Yin Sanpaku) – in Chinese "The Wolf Eye" Where the iris floats up under the upper eyelid from an abnormal

Left: the Three White Eye.

expansion of the eyeball. This person can be very shrewd and know exactly what they want and be astute enough to get it. They can act without consideration for the feelings of others. They are no strangers to conflict and will encounter opposition throughout their life, thus defining their ruthless determination.

Right: the Wolf Eye.

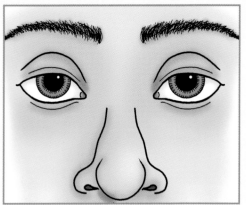

Where there is a large area of white under the eyeball, the physical or mental metabolism is becoming weaker or exhausted and mind, body and spirit are out of harmony. Intuition or the ability to assess people or situations is weak, so these people tend to put themselves in threatening or dangerous situations, and often not survive them. The danger seems to come from outside, which can lead to a fatal destiny. This tendency is increasing in young people and in drug addicts from the over-consumption of yin foods, and can be observed in those who are the object of misunderstanding, attacks or assassinations.

"The Four White Eye" refers to eyes that are prominent and bulge so there is white all around the iris. Possessors of this type of eye are adaptable and adept at handling unexpected situations but they can get angry if their personal plans are thwarted. They are good at anticipating events and working out alternative schemes and it is only when plan 'B' goes astray that they lose their cool.

Eyes looking to the side in opposite directions indicate an imbalance in the nervous system and can be caused by too many liquids, sugar or alcohol. This condition can develop into diabetes. They are accident-prone or victims of accidents (not the cause). They have difficulty in making decisions or feel "torn between two paths" in life.

Eyes crossed when relaxed or going to centre indicate that too much yang food like meat, cheese and salt are being consumed. This also indicates a deep psychological conflict within, which can make them become the cause of accidents because of their limited visions. Indications are a mind and body at war, or two sides of self at war, or an inability to settle conflict within the family.

THE EYEBROWS

These compare with the lifeline on the palm and signify happiness and longevity.

The shape of the eyebrows is determined by the underlying bone structure and therefore is an indication of the individual's constitution, vitality and mental energy.

The more animal foods the mother ate during pregnancy, the more the eyebrow slants down towards the nose. A more vegetarian diet tends to make them curve down at the outer edges.

If you lose your eyebrows, they fall away from the outside – therefore:
Length – signifies happiness and longevity
Thickness – signifies vitality, stamina and forcefulness
Fine eyebrows – signify sensitivity and possible weakness
The left eyebrow reflects a more paternal influence (the logical mind)
The right eyebrow reflects a more maternal influence (the creative mind).

Eyebrows and the lifeline

Eyebrows also reflect a person's constitution as they developed during pregnancy. The inner portion relates to the early stage of pregnancy, whereas the outer portion relates to the later stage. Since the course of life after birth generally repeats the growing process that took place during pregnancy, the sections of the eyebrow will reflect respectively from the centre out the youth, middle age and old age of a person's life.

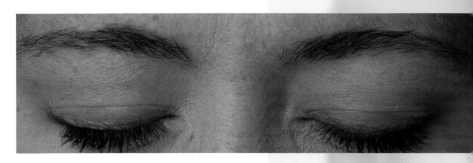

The space between the eyebrows

The amount of space between the eyebrows reflects what the mother ate especially during the third and fourth months of pregnancy. A small distance indicates more yang foods were eaten therefore excessive amounts eaten in life may have a detrimental effect on the solid organs in the body, particularly the liver, spleen and kidneys. The mind will become narrow with emotional sharpness and stubborn determination.

The wider the distance between the eyebrows indicates more yin foods were eaten at this time and if they are eaten in excess will affect the hollow organs, that is the stomach, gallbladder and bladder. This can lead to insecurity, uncertainty, indecision or lack of determination.

A very wide gap is called "the sign of the window" which indicates feelings of separation or a tendency to lead to separation in life.

Above: the shape of the eyebrows is determined by the underlying bone structure.

THE SHAPE OF THE EYEBROW

Smooth curving brows suggest a well balanced diet was eaten during pregnancy indicating physical and mental balance.

Crescent shaped – this person likes to make decisions intuitively and prefers to work with others.

Pointed eyebrows – this person is innovative and determined and likes to do everything better than the next person.

Eyebrows that splay out at the ends can indicate a thyroid problem.

Below: the amount of space between the eyebrows reflects what the mother ate especially during the third and fourth months of pregnancy.

Peaked eyebrows mean the person is active socially and physically but is gentle and sometimes timid in mentality. Later in their life they will become occupied with more mental and spiritual things.

The length of hair – the longer the hairs the more mentally and spiritually active the person is in character, while shorter hairs indicate a more physically active character.

Hair growing in different directions indicates a restless mind and someone who needs help focusing on their goals.

Changes in colour apart from in old age indicates sweating of excessive body salts or mineral depletion so have this checked.

Hair between the eyebrows suggests that during the third and forth months of pregnancy a lot of dairy and animal foods were eaten. Therefore this person can be affected by too much consumption of animal food, oily or fatty foods or dairy foods later in their life.

The eyebrows compare with the lifeline on your palm so a disconnected or broken eyebrow line can indicate the possibility of developing a serious sickness at some time in life.

The Chinese refer to the nose as the emperor of the face and it is considered important for it to be in balance with the rest of the features.

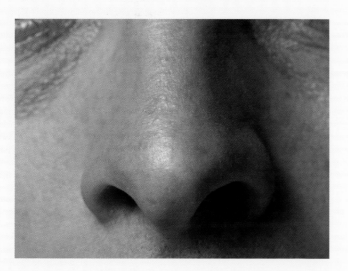

Left: the entire nose is said to reflect the spine.

THE NOSE REFLECTS THE CONDITION OF THE NERVOUS SYSTEM

The entire nose is said to reflect the spine. The muscles of the back, neck, shoulders and face are intimately connected; if there is stress along the spine the back muscles will compensate and this will be reflected in our posture, the way we hold our shoulders and in our faces. When the muscles of the face are affected by stress the features naturally change, and if the stress is severe enough it will pull the nose in one direction or the other.

THE NOSE EXPRESSES THE CONDITION OF THE CIRCULATORY SYSTEM

The tip of the nose represents the heart and its functions (refer to the fire element).

Nose swollen at the tip can mean the circulatory or excretory organs are under stress.

If it looks soft and watery, avoid too many liquids and tropical fruits. If the swelling seems fatty and hard, it can indicate sinus problems, or that the area around the heart is accumulating fat deposits or becoming inflexible so avoid fats, butter and cheeses.

Nose hardening at the tip can indicate hardening of the arteries or an accumulation of fat around the heart or major organs so reduced the intake of saturated fats especially from animal foods, eggs and dairy products.

The cleft nose is when the tip of nose has a split or indentation which is caused by nutritional imbalance especially a shortage of minerals and complex sugars during pregnancy. It can indicate the right and left sides of the heart are not coordinated which can cause an irregular heartbeat or murmur. Avoid the excessive intake of fruits, juices, coffee, refined sugars and soft drinks all of which deprive the body of minerals. Eliminate excessive stress or extremes and reduce the consumption of fats and cholesterol, which can cause plaque to build up in the arteries and clog them up.

Enlarged and swollen nose with red spots or hairs indicates a heart weakened by the over-consumption of alcohol.

Pale swollen tip of nose indicates a heart swollen by excess dairy food, rich food or cholesterol or perhaps too much caffeine.

Red tip results from the expansion of blood capillaries due to excessive intake of liquid, alcohol, stimulants, aromatic beverages and seasonings and this can lead to irregular blood pressure and hypertension.

Purple tip a more extreme case of the above, often indicates low blood pressure or heart failure.

White tip indicates contraction of heart and blood capillaries. Avoid salt and increase liquids and vegetables. It can indicate a hesitating mentality and coldness in the peripheral areas of the body, including fingers and toes.

Yellow or white pimples on any part of the nose tell us to avoid animal fat and dairy products as the digestive and excretory functions have become overloaded.

THE NOSE INDICATES THE HEALTH OF THE DIGESTIVE SYSTEM

The middle and upper part of the nose represents the stomach. If the area becomes red, it can denote heat in the stomach so avoid drinking or eating food that's too hot or spicy or having excessive alcohol and coffee.

The top of the nose is in the centre and deepest area of the face and corresponds to the pancreas, the deepest organ in the centre of the body. It is also said to reflect the true feelings and thoughts we have about ourselves. It can indicate the presence of hypogly-caemia, in which case one should avoid refined sugars, fruits and fruit juices till it subsides.

Nostrils represent the constitu-tional strength of our lungs and the gateway for oxygen to the lungs.

Nostrils that are well developed show large lungs, where there is a good capacity to take in oxygen. There is strength and potential in life, determination and courage as well as a more masculine yang nature.

Wide, plump and full nostrils are a sign of a strong libido.

Less developed nostrils show sensitivity, gentleness and a more feminine nature, which in extreme cases can indicate cowardice. In men it can indicate lack of vitality or a tendency towards homosexuality. In modern times nostrils are changing from the well developed to the less developed type.

Abnormally over-developed nostrils can indicate a violent character. In the case of a woman it suggests a tendency towards lesbianism.

Uneven nostrils indicate lungs that differ in size on the corresponding side. The groove at the sides of the nostrils reflects the condition of the bronchi. If this area becomes red, inflamed or spots occur avoid dairy products, sugar and chemical additives and increase consumption of green leafy vegetables and get plenty of fresh air and rest.

Hairy nostrils are an indication of excess animal foods; this person's nature will be competitive, spendthrift or easy come, easy go. They will achieve success not once but many times. This person doesn't succumb to despair.

Below: a straight and longer nose shows more sensitive nervous quality.

GENERAL CHARACTERISTICS

The shape of the nose can tell us much about the way we think and subsequently behave.

Normal well formed nose with average length and roundness shows a balanced mentality and good fortune.

Large nose shows a capacity for thinking.

Straight and longer nose shows more sensitive nervous quality.

Thin nose is indicative of someone with an independent nature, inwardly shy but who may not show it. They may be ill at ease in company and have difficulty in revealing enough of their personality to make friends.

Thin, beak-like nose high in the centre of the face is a sign of a lover of luxury who has to be careful this does not lead to them spending more they can afford.

Bony nose. If the nasal bones are clearly visible or the nose seems bony this person may find it difficult to accept advice and withdraw into themselves rather than struggle against opposition.

Short, flat nose shows a tendency to be determined and rigid in their thinking.

Soft, rounded nose is the mark of someone who has a sympathetic, warm and loving nature. They are free with compassion, good advice and money but can be a soft touch or be taken advantage of.

Raised or mounded sides on the nose indicate cloudy, fuzzy or unclear thinking.

HEIGHT OF THE NOSE

High nose indicates a tendency to be proud, competitive, prejudiced and discriminating. In the case of a woman it indicates a tendency towards frigidity or inability to conceive.

Lower, flatter nose indicates a person who is more generous and accepting of differences.

SHAPE OF NOSE AND PERSONALITY

The eagle nose resembles that of a bird of prey, hooked and sharp, curving outwards at the top.

This person relishes challenge, rarely backs away from an argument or large projects, is self-confident and formidable, can be intolerant with the inefficiencies or lack of purpose of others, makes their own luck and strides towards goals. Can be aggressive, self-centred and restless, in which case reduce the consumption of poultry and eggs.

Nose with an upward tilt
Sharp thinker but at times narrow- and short-sighted. Circumstances may make them self-reliant and settle for less than they would like in life. They are proud and can find it difficult to receive support or assistance in which case avoid too much fish and seafood (especially shell-fish and eggs

which will increase the shell-like wall they have around them).

Sharp pointed nose with tip pointing forwards can indicate an excitable nervous condition or weakness of the heart and circulation. They can be aloof and unapproachable or be hard to get to know. They may have had a tempestuous early family life and find it hard adapting to situations but they are generally successful in life. It is best for them to avoid processed, sugary and baked foods and excessive alcohol consumption.

Drooping nose indicates someone who is shrewd and is always on the look out for an opportunity and ideas that can be a little too ambitious for their own good so they may not make as much as they dream. They dislike responsibility and go a long way to avoid trouble. It is best for them to avoid excessive consumption of fruits, salad and liquids, as there is a tendency for a weak heart.

If the tip hangs down so that you cannot see both nostrils from the front it indicates a tendency towards nervousness, sensitivity and a changeable mind.

If the tip hangs down so that you can see both nostrils from the front it denotes a more wild character with a tendency towards narrow or unstable thinking.

Lump on the bridge of the nose shows a strong-willed person who thinks they know best and find it hard to act on the advice of another. They are open with their resources and have a generous heart and win good friends and allies in their life.

A crooked nose can result from an inharmonious physical or mental condition of the parents. This person can suffer mixed fortunes or sudden reversals of fate. This type of person learns to be resilient and handle these twists and turns in fortune or relationships. Life will never be boring and they learn to be survivors.

Left: a drooping nose indicates someone who is shrewd and is always on the look out for an opportunity

THE EARS

When we look at the ears we are looking at much more than an instrument of hearing. Our ears are unique like our fingerprints and represent much about our constitutional makeup.

In oriental medicine they are seen as a microcosm of the body and a miniature version of the embryo resting in the womb head downwards.

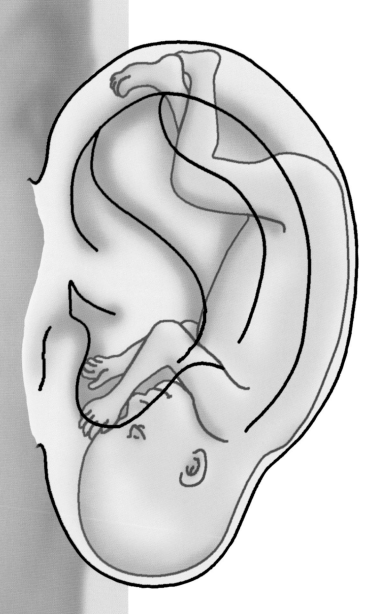

The ear lobe represents the head and face area. The outer rim represents the circulatory system, the spine in the middle represents the nervous system and round the entrance to the ear hole represents the strength of the digestive system. We can therefore gain an insight into the constitutional strength and mental aspects of these major systems.

The larger and fleshier your ears are, the more robust your constitution and balanced thinking. If such a person guards their health, they will have good fortune in life.

You will see Buddha depicted with long beautiful ears, round at the top, wide in the middle and tapered to long lobes like heavy pendulums down to his shoulders. To the oriental diagnostician this symbolises the inherited wealth of the Buddha nature, revealing the secret spiritual wealth with which Buddha entered this life.

Small ear lobe or no ear lobe indicates a less robust constitution because of lack of minerals during gestation, reflecting a narrower view of life. There is a tendency to gravitate towards more technical professions or a preference for more solitary work. They may have driving ambition, which can exclude other areas of their life, and can experience difficulties in understanding others.

Thick wide rim to the ear – Someone with a strong, well-developed circulatory system and a well-regulated body temperature. On an emotional level, this person is stable, strong and will circulate well with others and does not feel threatened.

No outer rim – Someone with a weaker circulatory system who does not circulate well with others and may be cautious.

The inner ridge inside the rim represents the nervous system. If the ridge is well developed, the person's system is strong and they have a sharp mind and a capacity to study and learn.

The centre of the ear – this ridge runs from the edge to the ear hole and corresponds to the strength of the digestive organs. When this line is well defined it indicates strong intestine; the person

possesses "guts" and has great courage, and a capacity to digest life and understand it.

The small flap of cartilage at the front centre of the ear, if well developed and protruding more than usual, indicates a strong will, tolerance and perseverance.

The ears are about the same size and shape as the kidneys themselves and reveal their constitutional strength. They distribute energy or chi throughout the body. It is said that a person's life unfolds from their kidneys, representing their ancestral inheritance in the form of talents and opportunities, the root of the direction of their life.

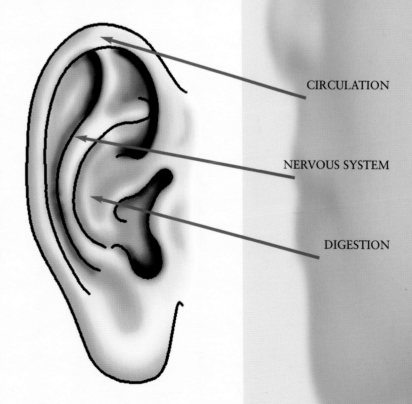

CIRCULATION

NERVOUS SYSTEM

DIGESTION

Below: when we look at the ears we are looking at much more than an instrument of hearing. our ears are unique like our finger-prints and represent much about our constitutional makeup.

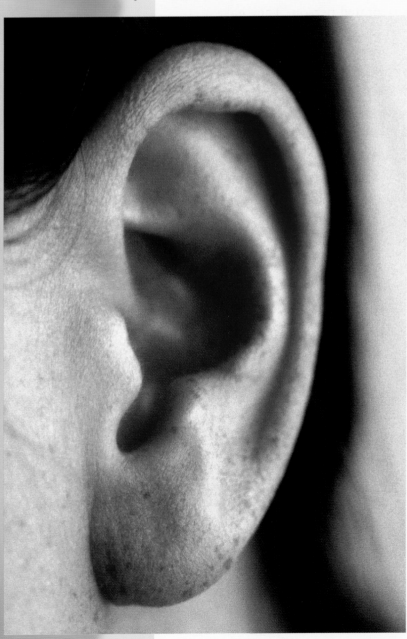

In Japan it is believed that to be a good listener, you must have strong kidneys.

In oriental diagnosis, the ear should be large and well shaped, round at the top, wide in the middle and tapering to an ample ear lobe.

Small ears indicate a more delicate physical constitution. This person seems to think more conceptually and take account of immediate problems rather than taking the broader view of situations and their meanings.

Ears that stick out indicate a more yin constitution so this person will develop more mental activity than physical. If the angle is greater than 30 degrees this can indicate scepticism and discrimination.

Ears that lie flat and close to the head indicate a person able to hear all sides and make sound judgments. Many great leaders had such ears.

Pointed ears indicate a person who has a sharp intellect and a tendency to be highly suspicious of others. Critical or aggressive, they are apt to think that defence is the best weapon. They are inclined to see the darker side of others and can fall prey to paranoia.

Red ears can mean the adrenals are under stress. Cut down on stimulants and caffeine.

Purple ears suggest a weak circulation, so it is best to avoid sugar, alcohol and extremely yin foods.

THE PHILTRUM

Below our nose is a small vertical cleft called the philtrum that connects our nose to our mouth. When we are inside the womb, during much of our gestation, we resemble a fish with our eyes on the side of our head and our mouth across the entire lower part of our face.

Gradually the powerful yang force closes our face up, our nose fuses, our mouth becomes smaller and the philtrum is formed, serving to remind us of the powerful force that brought us into being. If the yang force is strong, the philtrum is deep. If the force is less strong, it is more shallow and faint. Therefore in Oriental diagnosis the philtrum represents our constitution, reflects how fertile we are likely to be and indicates our prospects of good fortune and longevity. It is said to be the channel directing the energies from the emperor (the nose) to the mouth and is reputed to be especially relevant to the 50th year of life.

A deep philtrum indicates deep constitutional strength and an ambitious, focused and goal-orientated person. They have a strong appetite for life, sex and food and these appetites are more pronounced when the distance between the nose and lips is long. If it is very prominent, overwhelming energy can drive them.

A light and shallow philtrum indicates a more yin constitution. They are gentler and prefer to work more with their minds than their bodies. They tend to have fewer children and more slender means. For good fortune not to elude them they need to parcel out their life force to achieve their goals.

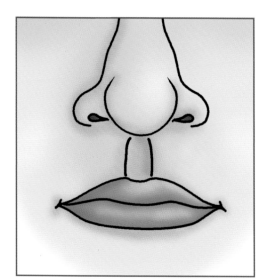
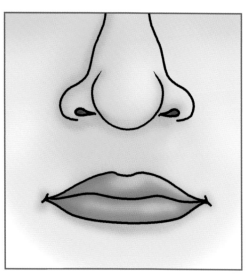

Left: examples of a deep and shallow philtrum.

Long, deep philtrum indicates fertility, good fortune and a long life. The area above the mouth represents the reproductive system, and in women the philtrum is specifically related to the uterus.

Narrow at mouth broadening to nose denotes someone born less strong but whose health gains strength. They have fewer children, as their energy is slightly restricted.

Right: philtrum broadening to nose, narrowing to nose (below right) and flaring in the middle (far right).

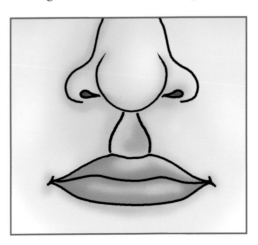

Wide at mouth narrowing to nose denotes someone born strong whose health weakens. Chinese face reading says it indicates having more sons than daughters.

Flaring in the middle indicates someone born weak whose middle life health is strong but who weakens again later. The Chinese regard this as the lake of stillness to indicate the person has an area of stagnation around the age of 50, which could mean depression or a loss.

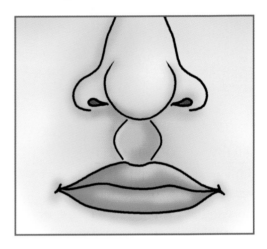

Short, strong philtrum indicates a shorter life but one with remarkable achievements in it.

Fading philtrum can indicate loss, illness or isolation.

Bent philtrum can mean the holder loses direction in life and experiences frustrated purpose or failure, depression or financial hardship. It is also an indication in women of a tilted uterus, broken relationships, a sagging pelvis or resentment towards men.

Creased philtrum indicates worrying times.

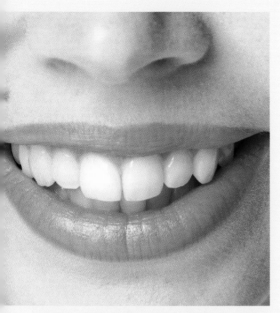

AREA ABOVE THE UPPER LIP

This area corresponds to the sex organs. If a woman grows a moustache, it means that the sex organs are troubled and may be clogged with too much protein and mucus. They can have trouble becoming pregnant, so need to cut out mucus-producing foods such as dairy foods and cut down excessive animal protein so that the ovum can implant itself and not get clogged with mucus. A woman with a hairy chin indicates a hormonal imbalance so she should avoid overeating especially too much fatty food.

The mouth and lips show both the general constitution and the current condition of the digestive organs and the entire digestive tract including the elimination of any undigested and unabsorbed foods and fluids.

Where the upper lip meets the skin, if this area is obscured the stomach is weak and needs protecting.

A swollen upper lip indicates the stomach is expanded or if red then it is inflamed so avoid sugar, spices and chew well (see p.79) and avoid bending forwards when eating.

A hardness and white colour around the border of the upper lips indicates stubbornness, overeating or chaotic eating. Eat less and avoid extremes of yin and yang foods.

The lower lip should ideally be full and wet.

An expanded upper lip can mean that peristalsis is weak leading to diarrhoea or constipation.

Tightness of the upper lip indicates a tendency towards constipation or holding on to emotions or expressions of disagreement. Avoid excess animal food, baked food and salt. Refer to the self-help chart and use the water element to draw energy round.

Purple colour of lips indicates hardness and inactivity of organ function, shyness as well as lack of energy in intestines caused by cold foods, liquids and medication.

Left: the area above the upper lip corresponds to the sex organs.

Sores in the corner of the mouth correspond to the duodenum and reveal too much fat is being consumed and there is an excessive secretion of bile.

A small mouth indicates a yang constitution or that the digestive system is loosing strength.

A tight mouth indicates the intestines are tight or in women that the vagina is tight.

Below: sagging corners of the mouth can be an indication of spleen weakness.

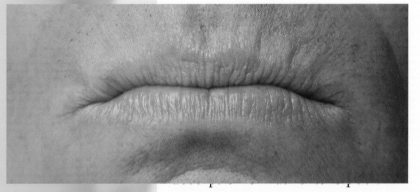

Right: chewing produces saliva, which is alkaline and not only starts off the process of digestion, but breaks up the food so that the stomach has less work to do.

Sagging corners of the mouth can be an indication of spleen weakness. (Refer to the self-help section on the earth element.) In the case of women it can indicate a weakness in the ovary on the sagging side, so avoid dairy foods, the birth control pill and stimulants.

The ideal size of the mouth
When you draw parallel lines vertically through the centre of the pupils the lines should touch the ends of the mouth. If the ends extend further than the lines, this person has a big mouth.

THE IMPORTANCE OF CHEWING

We should chew every mouthful 35–50 times. This is because chewing produces saliva, which is alkaline and not only starts off the process of digestion, but breaks up the food so that the stomach has less work to do. It also protects the stomach from the acid produced to break down the protein. If we fail to chew, the stomach has no protection and ulcers are formed.

If we drink too much with our meals we wash away the digestive juices. Then food is not properly digested and broken down so we get less goodness from it and the digestive organs have to work harder!

THE TONGUE

Observing the tongue is one of the main forms of diagnosis used in traditional medicine, as it reveals much about the present condition of our health and our mental constitution.

Most of the human body is covered by tough skin that does not change much from day to day. The tongue, however, is where the mucus membranes can be seen on the surface. These mucous membranes and the skin around them are highly sensitive and capable of rapid change, Any changes in our health, especially those that affect mucus production in our bodies, will affect the skin around the mucus membranes making it crack or discharge mucus. When stuck out, the tongue should be clear with a thin white coating and not tremble. Listed here is some information we can gain from this form of observation.

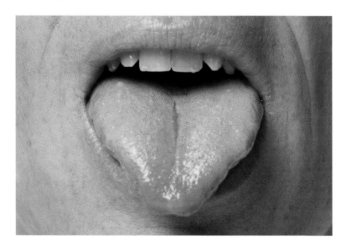

Left: when stuck out, the tongue should be clear with a thin white coating and not tremble.

THE MOVEMENT OF THE TONGUE AND OUR SPEECH

Speech is related to the heart and the cardiovascular system. Good enunciation indicates a strong heart.

Slurred speech indicates some type of cardiovascular problem including a murmur, irregular heartbeat, angina or an inadequate blood supply to the brain.

Sudden stuttering can reveal a lack of rhythm in life, or a heart weakened by consumption of too much liquid (water controlling fire).

Cut down on liquids, keep food simple and reduce the use of extreme foods, fats and red meat. Restore rhythm and regularity in your life. It can help to have a clock or something with a regular beat in the room or playing drums or dancing to establish rhythms to support the fire element.

Quivering tongue indicates a chi deficiency.

THE TONGUE

THE SHAPE OF THE TONGUE

The shape of the tongue gives us information on our mental constitution.

A wide tongue with a round tip indicates a person who is generally harmonious, gentle and understanding.

A narrow tongue with a sharp pointed tip indicates a person who has a tendency to be physically rigid or tight, mentally aggressive or offensive (hence the saying "they have a sharp tongue!"). Reduce the intake of salt, cheese, red meat and eat more vegetables (to reduce the wood element fuelling the fire element!)

Tongue with a divided tip indicates a person with a tendency to be indecisive and changeable ("speaks with fork tongue!") so support the wood and fire elements.

Thick tongue indicates a person with a more active, offensive or aggressive character who should avoid excessive fats and animal protein.

Stiff or deviated tongue indicates tension in the body on the deviated side or internal wind (balance the wood element).

Tooth marks at the side indicate a spleen deficiency. (Support the earth element.)

COLOUR OF TONGUE

This usually indicates our internal condition which might have lasted some time but which can change in a few weeks as the condition improves.

Pale red – normal

Red – internal heat

Purple – stagnant blood

Blue/black – internal cold

Pale – deficient condition

Right: the geography of the tongue.

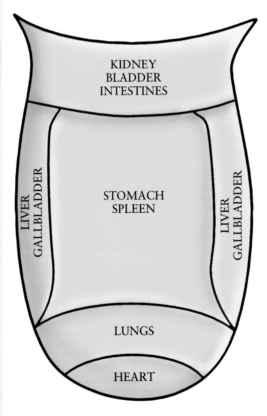

KIDNEY
BLADDER
INTESTINES

LIVER
GALLBLADDER

STOMACH
SPLEEN

LIVER
GALLBLADDER

LUNGS

HEART

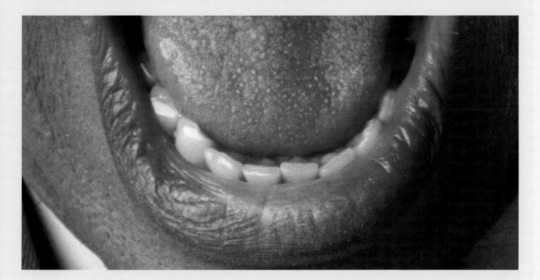

Left: the coating and texture of the tongue indicates our internal environment.

COATING AND TEXTURE

This indicates our internal environment.

Normal – thin white coating and slightly moist

Swollen – damp is present in the body.

Thick white coating – indicates internal cold.

Yellow coating – indicates internal heat.

No coat – when the tongue has a peeled look this indicates yin deficiency.

Wet – damp is present in the body.

Sticky – phlegm is present in the body.

Dry – heat is present or there is dehydration.

Pimples on the tongue are caused by the elimination of excessive protein, fat, or sugar. This can come about after combining a lot of fish and fruit, flour and dairy food or eggs and citrus juices.

Sores on the tongue indicate spleen or stomach problems caused by the over-consumption of too many acidic foods such as spices, tomato sauce, eggplant, peppers and sugar.

The geography of the tongue can give us an indication of the condition of specific organs.

THE VOICE

Noise is an expression of life, but it can reveal to us imperfections in function or construction. A machine makes all kinds of noises if it is faulty or being used incorrectly. The voice is the body's form of expression. For example, when you are speaking to someone on the telephone you can sense if there is something wrong by the flat tone in their voice.

Below are some examples:

ELEMENT AND ORGANS	VOICE QUALITY
WOOD **LIVER AND GALLBLADDER**	Shouting, clipped, sharp, empathic or loud indicates an excess of the wood element. A lack of, or repressed, wood is displayed by an inability to depart from a soft placatory voice.
FIRE **HEART AND SMALL INTESTINE**	Excess fire is often manifested by inappropriate laughter or giggling, also by fast or hysterical speech rising in pitch. Lack of fire can be indicated by a dull monotone without expression or joy.
EARTH **STOMACH, SPLEEN AND PANCREAS**	Imbalance in the earth element is manifested by an up and down singsong quality as if the person were trying to comfort someone. Also typified by an inability to complete sentences or sighing.
METAL **LUNG AND LARGE INTESTINE**	Imbalance in metal gives the voice a weeping, crying or plaintive tone with a lack of power. Or it can have a gasping or breathy quality.
WATER **KIDNEY AND BLADDER**	Imbalance in the water element makes the voice tremble and sound fearful or weak. Also gives rise to a sound like a groaning quality from deep inside the bones.

Personal empowerment begins when you take control of your life.

R ather than getting caught up in complicated scientific solutions so often simple changes in diet and lifestyle can have the most profound effect on our health, self-esteem and well-being.
Identify the organ/system that needs supporting and use the recommendations in this self-help section and in the "Food and the Five Tastes" chart.

Choose the appropriate key words for the element you are supporting and use them regularly as affirmations, for example "I am..." or "I have..."

LIFESTYLE SOLUTIONS FOR ELEMENTS

Everyday we are spending our life force so we should learn to spend it on the things that really matter.

Style: Emphasise the cooking style for each element. This will help balance the internal environment and support the organs, especially at the corresponding time of year.
Taste: A little of the taste will stimulate and benefit the organs but excess will stimulate or control the opposite element, for example too much salt will affect the heart.
Colours: Orange foods such as squash and carrots are good for the earth element (stomach and spleen), green vegetables are good for the wood element (liver and gallbladder).

The adverse internal environment for:
Fire is heat so avoid overheating foods such as fats and red meats, especially in a hot climate.
Earth is damp so avoid refined sugars and dairy foods that create internal dampness.
Metal is dry so avoid central heating and too many baked foods such as bread and biscuits.
Water is cold so avoid iced and refrigerated food and drink, especially in winter.
Wood is wind so avoid overeating, eating late, eating leftovers or re-heated foods that cause stagnation and fermentation in the intestines and produce internal wind.

FOOD AND THE FIVE TASTES

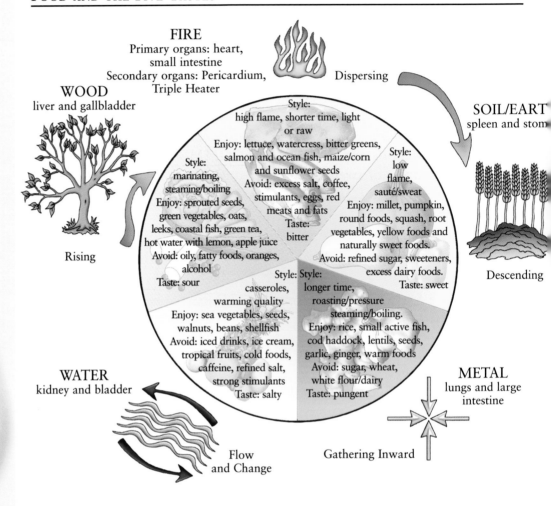

FIRE
Primary organs: heart, small intestine
Secondary organs: Pericardium, Triple Heater

Dispersing

WOOD
liver and gallbladder

SOIL/EART
spleen and stom

Style:
high flame, shorter time, light or raw
Enjoy: lettuce, watercress, bitter greens, salmon and ocean fish, maize/corn and sunflower seeds
Avoid: excess salt, coffee, stimulants, eggs, red meats and fats
Taste: bitter

Style:
marinating, steaming/boiling
Enjoy: sprouted seeds, green vegetables, oats, leeks, coastal fish, green tea, hot water with lemon, apple juice
Avoid: oily, fatty foods, oranges, alcohol
Taste: sour

Rising

Style:
low flame, sauté/sweat
Enjoy: millet, pumpkin, round foods, squash, root vegetables, yellow foods and naturally sweet foods.
Avoid: refined sugar, sweeteners, excess dairy foods.
Taste: sweet

Descending

Style:
casseroles, warming quality
Enjoy: sea vegetables, seeds, walnuts, beans, shellfish
Avoid: iced drinks, ice cream, tropical fruits, cold foods, caffeine, refined salt, strong stimulants
Taste: salty

Style:
longer time, roasting/pressure steaming/boiling.
Enjoy: rice, small active fish, cod haddock, lentils, seeds, garlic, ginger, warm foods
Avoid: sugar, wheat, white flour/dairy
Taste: pungent

WATER
kidney and bladder

METAL
lungs and large intestine

Flow and Change

Gathering Inward

WATER ELEMENT – KIDNEY AND BLADDER

Time of storage and rejuvenation.
Key words/affirmations:
courageous, curious, profound, adventurous, uninhibited, inventive.

RECOMMENDATIONS

- *Take exercise such as swimming or sports involving water.*
- *Take time to go on a retreat or to a health spa.*
- *Keep entertainment more restful such as the cinema (romantic films!).*
- *Communication with others can be more deep and profound with a slow cautious approach to relationships.*
- *Use oils such as jasmine and sandalwood in your bath.*
- *Take up meditation.*

- *Get plenty of rest, and for a few days try to fit in with the hours of daylight or go to bed before 10pm.*
- *Have periods of relaxation in the day to recharge, so you are not depleting yourself.*
- *Take time to reflect on things.*
- *Avoid stimulants and cut down on areas of stress, as drawing on these high levels of adrenalin drains and damages the kidneys.*
- *A sauna (or steam room) that induces sweating can reduce the load on the kidneys.*
- *Set goals and be a little adventurous to rediscover your courage.*

AVOID

- *Becoming overtired.*
- *Environments that are cold or damp.*
- *Too many changes at work, in relationships and environment till your energy has replenished.*
- *Procrastination.*
- *Excessive sexual activity.*
- *Becoming obsessive about secrecy.*

WOOD/TREE ELEMENT – LIVER AND GALLBLADDER

Time of the emergence of the new!
Key words/affirmations:
energetic, flexible, spontaneous, creative, thoughtful, patient, sensitive, humorous.

RECOMMENDATIONS

- *Keep life free and active.*
- *Focus on flexibility, motivation, growth and being light-spirited.*
- *Develop enthusiasm.*
- *Watch humorous films or television programmes.*
- *Springclean the mind and do an activity that is not in the normal pattern of your life.*
- *A detox diet is good for the liver, especially in spring.*
- *Shouting, dancing or supporting a team to relieve pent-up energy.*
- *Ideal exercises are competitive or racket sports and exercises that involve tensing and releasing muscles.*
- *Include a stretching routine to release muscular tension. t'ai chi is good for joint flexibility.*
- *Early morning exercise out of doors and prior to eating is good for the liver, especially under trees, which give off oxygen and energise the rising wood element.*
- *Recreation time can be more active, physical, challenging*

and energetic such as climbing, trekking and exploring the new.

- *Keep relationships spontaneous and communicative.*
- *Use oils such as grapefruit, chamomile and lavender.*

AVOID

- *Being obsessive about time or too fanatical about exercise.*
- *Stagnant, monotonous or pressurised lifestyles, which leave little possibility for creativity, innovation and humour.*
- *Overeating and eating late at night.*
- *Being overbearing and controlling.*

Below: avoid being obsessive about time or too fanatical about exercise.

FIRE ELEMENT – HEART AND SMALL INTESTINE

Time of full bloom/outgoing.
Key words/affirmations:
calm, adaptable, friendly, warm, peaceful, sociable, outgoing, charming, and joyful.

RECOMMENDATIONS

- *Re-establish some order, calm and rhythm in your life.*
- *Include means of self-expression such as dancing, singing, laughter and humour.*
- *Take up art or playing an instrument.*
- *Include exercise for the upper body and chest – cardio-vascular and team sports that involve being with others.*
- *Breathing exercises will support the heart.*
- *The martial aspect of t'ai chi will help relieve stress.*
- *Yoga builds up stamina and heat in the body.*
- *Spend time with others, family and friends.*
- *Do things that are socially interactive and get you noticed, have fun in groups or throw a party.*
- *Include in your life things that you are passionate about or find stimulating, inspiring or that make your heart sing.*
- *Allow time for outward expression but also time for rest, too.*

- *Develop a warm, comfortable, unconventional style! Make your living space the same.*
- *Massage the tip of your nose with the palm of your hand, and down the sides of the nose to enhance heart function and circulation.*

Oils are particularly good for the fire element:
Rose – anti-depressive, anti-inflammatory, balancing, calming, traditionally used as the herb of love, sexual and general tonic.

Rosemary – cardio tonic helps prevent hypertension, used in 1500s for bathing in to make you lively, lusty and joyful! Promotes circulation of chi and blood.

Strengthens heart beat and encourages flow of arterial blood,

Benefits cardiac fatigue, for example palpitations, low blood pressure and cold hands and feet (avoid if pregnant or breast-feeding).

Ylang ylang – a calming effect on the heart, works to clear heat.

Harmonises the shen (spirit) allowing it to express and experience joy.

Relieves nervous tension.

Promotes sleep and relieves agitation.

Helps reunite the emotional and sensual natures.

AVOID

- *Burning out and being chaotic in work and private life or letting things get out of control.*
- *Extremes of any kind, such as in behaviour, environment or food.*
- *Being isolated or alone.*
- *Becoming excessively self-indulgent or obsessed with your appearance.*

Below: oils are particularly good for the fire element

SOIL/EARTH ELEMENT – SPLEEN/PANCREAS AND STOMACH

Time for gathering and harvesting.

Key words/affirmations:
stable, transforming, having the power to concentrate and study,, helpful, understanding, resourceful, sympathetic, reliable and steady, nourished in life, supported and supportive, considerate, caring for others, self-respecting.

RECOMMENDATIONS

- *Make an effort to complete tasks, deal with unfinished issues, fulfil promises and resolve conflicts.*
- *Include activities that bring you nearer to the earth such as gardening, digging, walking, rambling, jogging or making clay pots.*
- *Ask yourself regularly whether your thoughts are nourishing and supporting you.*
- *Walk barefoot for 10 minutes a day on the earth to get a natural charge of energy (avoid if it is damp).*
- *Take up exercise to develop muscle tone or an exercise such as Pilates, which works on your core stability. Particularly work on strengthening your legs, which support you.*
- *Spend time with family and friends doing home-based things.*
- *Take self-catering or rural holidays.*
- *Take life at a slower pace and dine out occasionally with friends.*
- *Entertain and look after others but balance it with doing things just for you.*
- *Have regular massage, shiatsu, reflexology and aromatherapy.*
- *Like the stone in a piece of fruit, occasionally allow yourself to be in the centre of things.*
- *Keep your environment clutter-free and balanced.*
- *Encourage relationships that are supportive and caring.*
- *Develop compassion and warmth.*
- *Get out into nature.*
- *Have around you natural crystals, ceramics and other objects that come from the earth.*
- *Balance your home environment and include objects in pairs.*
- *Take up activities that boost self-confidence and self-esteem.*

AVOID

- *Working too hard, studying or having long periods of concentration without taking a break. Taking regular breaks gives you time to digest the information.*

- *Over-analysing things or situations.*
- *Becoming too dependent on others or having unrealistic expectations.*
- *Worry, obsession, self-doubt, over-extending yourself, meddling and being too protective.*
- *Leaving things unfinished – including sentences, conversations and projects.*
- *Burdening yourself.*
- *Becoming obsessive about food.*
- *Jealousy.*

METAL ELEMENT – LUNG AND LARGE INTESTINE

Time for withdrawing/letting go.
Key words/affirmations:
structured, disciplined, ordered, virtuous, discrete, authoritative, principled, having high standards, having sound judgment, beautiful, refined, with the capacity to shape and refine, precise.

RECOMMENDATIONS

- *Clear away finished projects and bring things to a conclusion.*
- *Sort out finances.*
- *Balance outward activities with inward activities such as yoga and t'ai chi.*
- *Learn breathing exercises and meditation.*
- *Create structure in your life.*
- *Communicate your ideas, thoughts and emotions. Get things off your chest.*
- *Focus on mental clarity.*
- *Practise letting go of what you no longer need in life to make more room for what sustains you.*
- *Skin brushing (skin is our third lung) or exfoliating will help and wear natural fibres so that the skin can breathe.*
- *Go for regular walks and have plenty of fresh air in your environment both at home and at work.*
- *Occasionally do things*

Left: get out into nature to help balance the earth element.

spontaneously.

- *Surround yourself with green plants to oxygenate the atmosphere during the day, but avoid them in the bedroom at night.*
- *Keep your environment functional, practical and simple.*
- *Take up exercises that focus on concentrating, strengthening the belly, increasing your breathing rate and which gets you out of doors, for example golf, rowing, running, cycling and stretches that open the lungs.*
- *For recreation go sight-seeing or on educational holidays.*
- *Join clubs or debating groups which involve relating to others and expression on an intellectual level.*
- *Therapies such as acupuncture, hypnotherapy and psychotherapy are helpful*
- *A style that will be comfortable for, and supports, this element is formality and order in clothes and surroundings.*

Bach Flower Remedies, which are particularly helpful, are:

Crab apple – for getting rid of impurities in body/mind.

Honeysuckle – if you are stuck in the past, helps you focus on the now.

Pine – used for regret.

Walnut – helps you to move on.

Oils:

Thyme – invigorates the lungs and spirit.

Eucalyptus – decongests.

Pine – cleanses, clears phlegm, is a tonic for the lungs and useful for asthma.

AVOID

- *Exposure to nicotine, carbon dioxide, lead and nitrogen dioxide.*
- *Central heating, which dries up the atmosphere (use a humidifier).*
- *Sitting still or slumped for long periods.*
- *Becoming autocratic, strict and pernickety, distant, too intense, formal or self-righteous.*
- *Putting yourself under intense pressure or feeling trapped in situations.*
- *Becoming isolated in your life or indifferent to the world outside yourself.*
- *Perfectionism or becoming obsessed with details.*

PRESSURE POINTS ON THE FACE

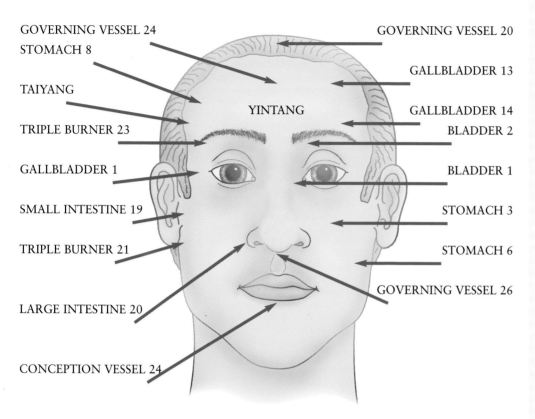

GOVERNING VESSEL 24
STOMACH 8

TAIYANG

TRIPLE BURNER 23

GALLBLADDER 1

SMALL INTESTINE 19

TRIPLE BURNER 21

LARGE INTESTINE 20

CONCEPTION VESSEL 24

YINTANG

GOVERNING VESSEL 20

GALLBLADDER 13

GALLBLADDER 14
BLADDER 2

BLADDER 1

STOMACH 3

STOMACH 6

GOVERNING VESSEL 26

Left: pressure points on the face. They each have a number corresponding to their position along the meridian.

GET STRAIGHT TO THE POINT

The vital flow of energy or Chi (Qi) within our body is essential to our health and well being. According to Oriental Theory it circulates along channels, 12 of which are connected to a particular organ, and are named after the organ to which they are linked. The Governing and Conception vessel meridians, located along the midline of the body, balance the Chi in the twelve main channels (see p.15). Specific pressure points along these meridians are where you can most easily manipulate the Chi using acupressure or touch to unblock, strengthen and calm the flow of Chi. They each have a number corresponding to their position along the meridian, a name and perform specific functions. The points on the face (listed below) can be used to relieve certain conditions as they act on the meridians that link the skin, sense organs and muscles of the face to the internal source of their problem – so they work on both the symptom and cause.

There are three main ways to treat these points:

To calm Chi – use the palm of your hand or apply light moving pressure for about 2 minutes.

To add energy to a point with your thumb or fingertip – apply stationary perpendicular pressure for two minutes.

To disperse or unblock Chi and encourage a smooth flow of Chi – apply pressure in a circular motion with fingertips or thumb for two minutes.

Most of the points are paired and symmetrical so you can massage these pairs at the same time using both hands, except the ones located along the midline of the body when there is only one. (Refer to the diagram – Pressure Points on the face)

Name, Meridian Number and Element Influenced	Location	Function
Stomach 3 – Juliao Big Bone Earth	Directly below pupil if looking straight forward, in groove under cheek bone.	Clears sinus and nasal congestion. Calms twitching eyelids.
Stomach 6 – Jiache Jaw Chariot Earth	In the centre of the masseter muscle when your teeth are clenched.	Eases tension in jaw and toothache
Stomach 8 – Touwei Head Support Earth	To the side of the head above the temples just in front of the hairline.	Clears a 'muzzy' or heaviness in the head caused by food or phlegm.
Large Intestine 20 – Yingxiang Welcome Fragrance Metal	In the grooves either side of the nostrils	Relieves nasal problems e.g. sneezing, sinusitis, runny or stuffed nose. Helpful for loss of smell.
Small Intestine 19 – Tinggong Listening Palace Fire	In the depression in front of the ear formed when you open your mouth.	Used for tinnitus, deafness, restricted movement of jaw and toothache.
Bladder 1 – Jingming Eye Brightness Water	In the depression slightly above the inner corner of the eye.	For redness, swelling and pain in the eye. Conjunctivitis, runny, swollen or dry eyes.

Name, Meridian Number and Element Influenced	Location	Function
Bladder 2 – Zanzhu Collecting Bamboo Water	On the middle end of the eyebrow in the little groove.	Brightens the eyes. Used for headaches behind the eye, blurred vision, floaters in front of the eye, glaucoma.
Triple Burner 21 – Ermen Ear Door Fire	In the depression behind the ear lobe.	Used to relieve tinnitus, deafness, glue ear and toothache.
Triple Burner 23 – Sizhukong Silk Bamboo Hole Fire	In the depression at the lateral end of the eyebrow.	Held with GB 1 relieves headache. Helpful for blurred vision and twitching of eyelids.
Gallbladder 1 – Tongziliao Pupil Crevice Wood	In the little depression outside the orbital bone at the outer corner of the eye.	Used to ease headache, migraines, red, dry, tired or painful eyes.
Gallbladder 13 – Benshen Mind Root Wood	Just in front of the hairline of the forehead above GB 14.	Calms the mind, relieves anxiety, constant worry and fixed thoughts. Effects enhanced if used with GV 24. Insomnia.
Gallbladder 14 – Yangbai Yang White	Directly above the pupil a thumb width above the middle of the eyebrow.	Used to relieve frontal headaches and hay fever.
Governing Vessel 20 – Baihui Hundred Meetings	On the midline of the head, at the midpoint connecting the apex of the two ears.	Used to clear/calm the mind if life feels chaotic, as it unites everything. Lifts depression and facial features, relieves helps piles.
Governing Vessel 24 – Shenting Mind Courtyard	In the middle of the forehead just in front of the hairline.	Used to ease insomnia, palpitations, anxiety and calms the mind particularly if used with GB 13.

Name, Meridian Number and Element Influenced	Location	Function
Governing Vessel 26 – Renzhong Middle of the Person	Two thirds of the way up the Philtrum from mouth to nose.	Revives vital life force, therefore used in cases of fainting or shock. Relieves facial puffiness and muscle strain especially in the lower back. In an emergency, rotate finger strongly anticlockwise.
Conception Vessel 24 – Chengjiang Saliva Receiver	In the groove below the lower lip.	Used for facial puffiness, swollen gums, and toothache.
Taiyang – Greater Yang	In a little depression about one finger's breadth behind the outer end of the eyebrow.	Used to relieve tension and temporal headaches and eye problems.
Yintang – Seal Hall	Midway between the middle ends of the eyebrows.	Calms the mind, allays anxiety, clears perception and improves concentration and memory.

DAO-YIN FOR THE HEAD, FACE AND NECK

Be still and close your eyes – with the tip of your tongue resting on your palate, inhale and then exhale deeply and become aware of your head, face and neck, noting how they feel.

Shake out your wrists and hands as if flicking water off them – as it is important to keep your wrists as loose as possible and the chi flowing to your fingertips when doing Dao-Yin.

The Brain – tap over your head with lose fists/ or tips of fingers, from the hairline over your head to the base of your skull, gradually working in lines starting from the midline outwards towards your ears. Ending by lightly tapping on GV20 on top of the head to stimulate circulation to the brain and lift depression.

The Forehead – massage lightly following your hairline around to your ears, focusing on GV24, GB13, and ST8. Massage Yintang between your eyebrows to calm the mind and GB14 above the centre of the eyebrows. Place your fingers lightly on the centre line of the forehead and stroke outwards to the temples (as if wiping away any worries). End lightly massaging Taiyang to relieve tension and support the spleen.

Eyebrows – pinch the eyebrows with thumb and forefinger beginning at the nose and ending at the temples. Press Triple Burner 23 at the ends of the eyebrows for headaches.

Eye Socket – with fingertips trace below the eyes around the sockets pressing lightly from the nose to the outer corner of the eyes to clear blocked sinuses. End by pressing Gallbladder 1 to ease headaches and tired eyes.

Cheeks – using a light circular motion of the fingertips work from Large Intestine 20 across the cheeks to Stomach 3 underneath the cheekbones for sinus congestion and generally over the cheeks to support the Lungs.

Nose – with a flat palm resting on the centre of your nose make a circle with the palm to massage the tip of the nose and with your fingers works down the sides of the nose to support the heart and circulation.

Gums and jaw – place the fingertips below the nose pressing GV 26 and massage outward over the top lip and gum to the other corners of the mouth using small circular movements to support your digestive function and the teeth. Do the same under the mouth starting at CV 24

tracing the line of the jawbone to the ears. This strengthens the gums. Work into the masseter muscle at the jaw in Stomach 6 to relieve facial tension and toothache. Press with a bent index fingers and the thumbs below the chin working around to the ears to support your salivary and lymph glands.

Ears – with a bent index finger and thumb squeeze around the ears and pull them up, back and down to support the kidneys. Then stroke over and around the back of the ears.

Neck – Massage with your middle finger under the occipital ridge at the back of the head where it joins the neck. Work from behind the ear towards the spine on each side. This area holds a lot of tension and this can relieve congestion and migraines. To ease tension in the muscles at the back of the neck, rest the heel of your hand on one side of the spine and the finger tips on the other, and gently squeeze. Then repeat with the other hand. Remember the neck is the bridge to the brain so it is important to keep it relaxed and free. Gently massage the thyroid gland in the front of the neck with the tips of the fingers.

Eyes – rub the palms of your hands together then place them over your eyes. This is a wonderful tonic for tired eyes and supports the Liver.

Then stop for a moment take a few deep breaths and feel how different your head feels.

INDEX